About this book

This book is designed to help you achieve your best result in the National Tests at the end of Key Stage 3. It targets the 3 – 5 tier of entry.

How to use this book

The units in this book are arranged in the same order as the National Curriculum so you can be sure it covers everything you need to know.

Use the **contents list** on the next page or the **index** at the end of the book to find the material you want.

The book provides:

Key information highlighted so you can see the important information at a glance, for example:

▶ To **multiply** a number by 10 move all the digits 1 place to the **left**.

10 has 1 zero

Worked examples showing the techniques you need to be able to use.

Plenty of questions so you can practise the techniques. The exercises are differentiated helping you to build up your skills and allowing you to revisit topics. The **A** exercises are more straightforward than the **B** exercises.

Investigations. There are four investigations in the book to help you practise your Using and Applying Maths skills. They can be found on pages 80, 92, 128 and 209.

Revision exercises at the end of each unit to help you identify areas of weakness so you can see what you need to revise. The **Review** column points you to the relevant material in the unit.

Practice SATS papers at the end of the book. The papers mirror the structure and question style of the real thing giving you valuable practice.

Answers to the exercises are provided in a separate answer book: ISBN 0 19 914568 7.

Contents

1 NUMBERS AND THE NUMBER SYSTEM

1.1 Place value

▶ This shows the values of each digit in the number 5246:

Th	H	T	U
5	2	4	6

▶ The digit 5 has a value of 5000.

▶ The digit 2 has a value of 200.

▶ The digit 4 has a value of 40 and there are 6 units.

▶ The number   5 246   in words is:

five thousand   two hundred and forty six

Exercise 1.1A

1 In the number 3524 what is the value of the digit 5?

2 For the number 2758 copy and complete this table.

Digit	Value
2	
7	
5	
8	

3 Give the value of the bold digit in each of these numbers?

   a 638**4**   **b** 5**7**06   **c** **8**527   **d** 6**9**74
   e **9**898   **f** 60**7**5   **g** 980**2**   **h** 7**6**68

4 Write each of these numbers in words.

   a 6834   **b** 7692   **c** 9075   **d** 3806

Exercise 1.1B

1 In the number 8675 what is the value of the digit 6?

2 Write the number 3564 in words.

3 Write this number in digits:
Five thousand four hundred and seven

4 Here are some clues for a 4-digit number:

- a digit has a value of 30
- a digit has a value of 700
- a digit has a value of 6000
- the units digit is 9

Write down the number.

You can extend place value to include millions.

▶ This shows the value of each digit in the number 7 403 126:

M	H Th	TTh	Th	H	T	U
7	4	0	3	1	2	6

▶ The digit 4 has value four hundred thousand.

▶ The digit 2 has value two tens which is twenty.

▶ The number   7 403 126   in words is:

seven million,   four hundred and three thousand,   one hundred and twenty six

Exercise 1.1C

1 In the number 1254 what is the value of the digit 5?

2 What is the value of the digit 6 in the number 6584?

3 What is the value of the bold digit in each of these numbers?

a 2453   b 15 383   c 7492   d 184 623
e 283 465   f 847 345   g 8 365 426   h 1 954 683

4 Consider the number 127 356.

a What is the value of the digit in the ten thousands position?
b Write the number in words.

5 Write this number in digits:

forty three thousand, five hundred and sixty six

6 Write each of these numbers in words.

a 4527   b 36 275   c 80 745   d 1 623 803

7 Make the largest number you can using all the digits
0, 6, 2, 5, 7, 3

Exercise 1.1D

1　In the number 206 548 what is the value of the digit 6?

2　Look at these numbers: 10 564 and 15 064
 a　Write each number in words.
 b　Which number is greater?

3　a　Write this number in digits:
   five thousand and three
 b　What number is 3000 more than part **a**?

4　Give the value of each digit in 2 563 407.

5　What number is 30 000 more than 75 650?

6　Use all the digits 0, 2, 4, 5, 6, 7, 8 to make:
 a　the largest number possible
 b　the smallest number possible
 c　a number in which the 2 stands for twenty thousand.

1.2 Multiplying by 10, 100, 1000, ...

▶ To **multiply** a number by 10 move all the digits 1 place to the **left**.

10 has 1 zero

Example 1

$134 \times 10 = 1340$

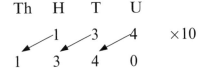

Exercise 1.2A

1　Multiply each number by 10.
 a 5746　　b 3825　　c 6362　　d 57 462　　e 38 125
 f 14　　　g 7　　　　h 354　　　i 756　　　j 8

2　One fence post is 324 cm long.
 What is the total length of 10 fence posts?

Exercise 1.2B

1 Multiply each number by 10.

   a 3000   **b** 40 004   **c** 300 000
   d 156 005   **e** 370 050   **f** 5 million
   g 10 010 010 **h** 750 000

2 A bridge is made up of ten sections.
   Each section weighs 350 000 kg.
   Give the total weight of all ten sections.

You can use a similar method to multiply by 100 and 1000.

▶ To multiply by 100 move all the digits 2 places to the left.

   100 has 2 zeros

Example 2
$745 \times 100 = 74\,500$

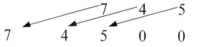

▶ 1000 has 3 zeros. So, to multiply a number by 1000 move
  all the digits 3 places to the left.

Example 3
5862×1000

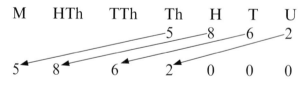

Fill in the empty spaces with zeros.

Exercise 1.2C

1 Multiply each of these numbers by 10.

   a 34   **b** 583   **c** 7391   **d** 46   **e** 84 560

2 Multiply each of these numbers by 100.

   a 7   **b** 20   **c** 164   **d** 562   **e** 6394

Note:
You should never use a
calculator to multiply by
10 or 100.

3 Multiply each of these numbers by 10 and by 100:

   a 656   **b** 1075   **c** 12   **d** 1001   **e** 30 400

4 Multiply six thousand and nine by one hundred.

5 Which is larger: 2560×100 or $26\,500 \times 10$?

6 The digit 4 in 1432 has the value 4 hundreds.
   Multiply 1432 by 1000.
   What value does the 4 digit have now?

Exercise 1.2D

1 What number multiplied by 10 gives 3540?

2 Copy and fill in: $3040 \times \boxed{} = 3\,040\,000$

3 Multiply each of these numbers by 10, 100 and 1000.

   a 286   **b** 10 405   **c** 65 101   **d** 30   **e** 200 400

4 One curb stone is 120 cm long. Give the total length of:

   a 10 stones   **b** 100 stones   **c** 1000 stones

5 There are 100 cm in a metre. How many cm are in:

   a 14 metres   **b** 960 metres   **c** 6007 metres?

6 **a** $3460 \times 10 \times 10 \times 10 =$
   b $34\,600 \times 100 =$
   c What can you say about the answers to parts **a** and **b**?

7 Multiply seventy thousand by one thousand. Give your
   answer in digits.

1.3 Dividing by 10, 100, 1000, ...

▶ To **divide** a number by 10 move all the digits 1 place to the **right**.

Example 1

$8650 \div 10 = 865$

Th	H	T	U
8	6	5	0
	8	6	5

$\div 10$

Exercise 1.3A _____

1 Divide each of these numbers by 10.

    a 70   **b** 300   **c** 420   **d** 5640

    e 36 200   **f** 7000   **g** 4 000 000   **h** 21 000

    i 36 500   **j** 4 million

2 Ten lottery winners share a prize of £3 075 420.
    How much does each winner get?

Exercise 1.3B _____

1 Divide each of these numbers by 10.

    a 6050   **b** 300 000   **c** 2 050 600

    d 10   **e** 900   **f** 1090

    g 4 175 040   **h** 81 600   **i** 1 510 040

    j 1 million

2 A relay team of 10 runners go in for a race.
    Each athlete runs the same distance.
    The race is 23 650 m long.
    What distance does each member of the relay team run?

You can use a similar method to divide by 100 and 1000.

▶ To divide by 100 move all the digits 2 places to the right.

Example 2

$728\,000 \div 100 = 7280$

HTh	TTh	Th	H	T	U
7	2	8	0	0	0
		7	2	8	0

▶ 1000 has 3 zeros. So, to divide a number by 1000 move
    all the digits 3 places to the right.

Example 3

$654\,000 \div 1000$

HTh	TTh	Th	H	T	U
6	5	4	0	0	0
			6	5	4

Exercise 1.3C _____

1 Divide each of these numbers by 10.
  a 470   **b** 17 340   **c** 29 000   **d** 500   **e** 19 060 000

2 Divide each number by 10, 100 and 1000.
  a 364 000   **b** 30 000   **c** 120 000   **d** 10 100 000

3 Which is larger: 12 000 ÷ 10 or 120 000 ÷ 1000?

4 Which is smaller: 784 000 ÷ 100 or 78 400 000 ÷ 1000?

5 What is 4 thousand divided by 100?

6 What is two million divided by one thousand?

7 Divide 450 000 by 100. Give your answer in words.

Exercise 1.3D _____

1 A number becomes 60 when divided by 100.
   What is the number?

2 100 people win £20 million on the lottery.
   How much does each winner get?

3 150 000 apples are packed in boxes.
   How many apples are in each box if there are:
   a 100 boxes   **b** 1000 boxes   **c** 10 boxes?

4 There are 1000 grams in a kilogram.
   How many kilograms are in:
    a 14 200 000 grams   **b** 230 000 grams   **c** 4 million grams?

5 Divide 560 000 by one thousand.

6 Divide one hundred and seven thousand by one hundred.
   Give your answer in digits.

7 Divide 120 000 000 by 10, then divide the answer by 1000.
   Give the last answer in words.

1.4 Multiplying and dividing by 20, 600, 5000, …

You can use what you know about multiplying by 10, 100 and 1000 to help you multiply by numbers like 20, 600 and 5000.

Example 1

Calculate 18×80

You can break $\times 80$ down into $\times 8$ then $\times 10$

$$18 \times 80 = 18 \times 8 \times 10$$
$$= 144 \times 10$$
$$= 1440$$

Example 2

Calculate 23×600

You can break $\times 600$ down into $\times 6$ then $\times 100$

$$23 \times 600 = 23 \times 6 \times 100$$
$$= 138 \times 100$$
$$= 13\,800$$

Example 3

Calculate 46×5000

You can break $\times 5000$ down into $\times 5$ then $\times 1000$

$$46 \times 5000 = 46 \times 5 \times 1000$$
$$= 230 \times 1000$$
$$= 230\,000$$

Exercise 1.4A _____

1 Calculate:

a 35×40	**b** 68×70	**c** 92×20	**d** 66×50	**e** 19×80
f 46×60	**g** 37×40	**h** 162×30	**i** 274×20	**j** 178×70

2 Calculate:

a 37×600	**b** 46×400	**c** 23×800	**d** 75×300	**e** 48×400
f 29×800	**g** 66×900	**h** 14×700	**i** 19×400	**j** 23×600

3 Calculate:

a 47×2000	**b** 19×4000	**c** 66×5000	**d** 19×6000	**e** 27×7000
f 24×8000	**g** 36×9000	**h** 47×3000	**i** 124×2000	**j** 620×3000

Exercise 1.4B

1 Films are packed in boxes of 35.
   How many films are there in 80 boxes?

2 A lorry moves 30 tonnes of stone each trip.
   It makes 70 trips.
   How many tonnes of stone in total does the lorry carry?

3 A plastic tray weights 46 grams.
   In total what is the weight of 6000 trays?

4 A machine makes 37 keyrings each minute.
   How many keyrings is this in each hour?

5 Bags of grass seed weigh 56 kg.
   A golf club buys 700 bags.
   Find the total weight of the bags it buys.

You can also use what you know about multiplying by 20, 600 and 5000 to help you divide by 20, 600 and 5000.

Example 4

Calculate $1640 \div 20$

$$1640 \div 20 = 1640 \div 2 \div 10$$
$$= 820 \div 2 \div 10$$
$$= 82$$

Example 5

Calculate $378\,000 \div 600$

$$378\,000 \div 600 = 378\,000 \div 6 \div 100$$
$$= 63\,000 \div 100$$
$$= 630$$

Example 6

Calculate $4\,575\,000 \div 5000$

$$4\,575\,000 \div 5000 = 4\,575\,000 \div 5 \div 1000$$
$$= 915\,000 \div 1000$$
$$= 915$$

Exercise 1.4C _____

1 Calculate:

    a $360 \div 20$ **b** $4750 \div 50$ **c** $164\,800 \div 40$ **d** $1840 \div 80$

    e $26\,400 \div 6$ **f** $5\,765\,000 \div 50$ **g** $2\,646\,800 \div 20$ **h** $96\,300 \div 30$

2 Calculate:

    a $48\,600 \div 200$ **b** $375\,000 \div 500$ **c** $720\,000 \div 600$ **d** $493\,500 \div 700$

    e $164\,800 \div 800$ **f** $344\,000 \div 400$ **g** $2\,624\,800 \div 200$ **h** $15\,000\,000 \div 500$

3 Calculate:

    a $24\,000 \div 2000$ **b** $1\,680\,000 \div 4000$ **c** $175\,000\,000 \div 5000$

    d $3\,654\,000 \div 6000$ **e** $49\,000\,000 \div 7000$ **f** $810\,000\,000 \div 9000$

Exercise 1.4D _____

1 125 000 bags of crisps are packed into 500 boxes.
Each box has the same number of bags.
How many bags are in each box?

2 Each hour a machine runs it makes 400 pens.
How long will it take the machine to make 124 000 pens?

3 A page of stamps holds 60 stamps.
354 000 stamps are printed.
How many pages is this?

4 Jan packs 40 000 films in 800 boxes.
How many films are in each box?

1.5 Negative numbers and the number line

Sometimes you need to describe a value that is less than zero.

Example 1

The temperature at 7 pm is 2°C.

At 9 pm the temperature has fallen by 5°C.

What is the temperature at 9 pm?

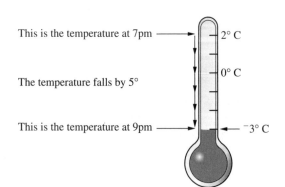

This is the temperature at 7pm ⟶   2° C

The temperature falls by 5°   0° C

This is the temperature at 9pm ⟶   ⁻3° C

The temperature at 9 pm is ⁻3°C.

A number less than zero has a negative sign.

Exercise 1.5A _____

1 Copy and complete this table.

Temperature °C	Change °C	New temperature °C
3°	fall by 6°	
5°	fall by 8°	
2°	fall by 7°	
⁻2°	fall by 4°	
⁻6°	fall by 2°	
0°	fall by 8°	

2 The temperature at 6 am is ⁻4°C.
By 9 am the temperature has risen by 5°C.
What is the temperature at 9 am?

Exercise 1.5B _____

1 Copy and complete this table.

Temperature °C	Change °C	New temperature °C
5°	fall by 8°	
⁻3°	fall by 2°	
⁻2°	rise by 5°	
⁻3°	rise by 2°	
⁻8°	rise by 6°	
5°	fall by 12°	
0°	fall by 7°	
⁻1°	rise by 18°	

▶ Negative numbers are all the numbers less than zero.

▶ You can show positive and negative numbers on a number line.

Some people say *minus* 3 instead of *negative* 3.

Negative numbers ——— Positive numbers

⁻5 ⁻4 ⁻3 ⁻2 ⁻1 0 1 2 3 4 5

The number ⁻3 is a unique point on the number line and is called *negative* 3.

Exercise 1.5C

1 Copy and complete:

a | ? | ⁻2 | ⁻1 | ? | ? | ? |

b | ⁻8 | ? | ⁻6 | ? | ? | ? |

c | ? | ? | 0 | 1 | ? | ? |

d | ? | ? | ? | 1 | ? | 3 |

e | ? | ? | ⁻1 | ? | ? | ? |

f | ? | ? | ? | 2 | ? | ? |

g | ? | ? | ⁻6 | ? | ? | ? |

h | ? | ? | ? | ? | ⁻8 | ? |

i | ? | ? | ? | 0 | ? | ? |

j | ? | ? | ? | ⁻10 | ? | ? |

2 For each part, start with a number line like this.

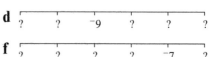

-10   0   10

On a number line show all the whole numbers:

a from ⁻4 to 3   **b** from ⁻6 to 1

c from ⁻7 to 1   **d** from ⁻8 to ⁻1

e from 5 to ⁻4.   **f** from 4 to ⁻2.

g from 8 to ⁻7   **h** from ⁻10 to 5

i from ⁻1 to 1   **j** from 7 to ⁻7

3 On a number line for each part show all the whole numbers:

a from ⁻2 to 3   **b** from 5 to ⁻4

c from 0 to ⁻5   **d** from 3 to ⁻1

e from ⁻6 to ⁻4   **f** from ⁻5 to ⁻11

g from ⁻4 to 0   **h** from ⁻2 to 2

i from ⁻6 to 6   **j** from ⁻7 to 0

Exercise 1.5D

1 Copy and complete:

a | ? | ? | ? | ⁻3 | ? | ? |

b | ? | ? | ⁻7 | ? | ? | ? |

c | ? | ? | ? | ? | 2 | ? |

d | ? | ? | ⁻9 | ? | ? | ? |

e | ? | ? | ? | ? | ? | 1 |

f | ? | ? | ? | ? | ⁻7 | ? |

g | ? | ? | ? | ? | 0 | ? |

h | ? | ? | ⁻19 | ? | ? | ? |

i | ? | ? | ? | ⁻5 | ? | ? |

j | ? | ? | ? | ⁻100 | ? | ? |

2 For each part, start with a number line like this.

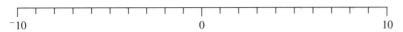

On a number line show all the whole numbers:

a from ⁻6 to 2   **b** from ⁻3 to 4
c from ⁻2 to 5   **d** from ⁻5 to ⁻3
e from 1 to ⁻6   **f** from 1 to ⁻1
g from 9 to ⁻2   **h** from ⁻10 to ⁻8
i from ⁻3 to 0   **j** from 6 to 9

3 On a number line for each part show all the whole numbers:

a from ⁻3 to 2   **b** from 4 to ⁻6
c from 2 to ⁻1   **d** from 4 to ⁻3
e from ⁻8 to ⁻5   **f** from ⁻3 to ⁻12
g from ⁻7 to 0   **h** from ⁻5 to 3
i from ⁻8 to 5   **j** from ⁻9 to 0

1.6 Putting numbers in order

You can order numbers using a number line.

Say you start at ⁻3 on the line.

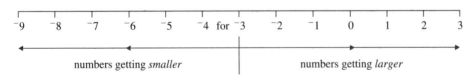

Numbers *smaller* than ⁻3 are: ⁻4, ⁻5, ⁻6, ⁻7, ⁻8, ... all
numbers on the *left*.

Numbers *larger* than ⁻3 are: ⁻2, ⁻1, 0, 1, 2, 3, ... all
numbers on the *right*.

Example

Order these numbers: ⁻4, 3, 0, ⁻5, 1, ⁻1, 2.
Start with the smallest.

Put these numbers on a number line:

- The number furthest to the *left* is   ⁻5 (the smallest number).

- The number furthest to the *right* is   3 (the largest number).

- Now fill in the others.

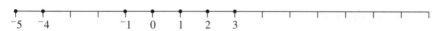

- Starting with the smallest the order is: ‾5, ‾4, ‾1, 0, 1, 2, 3

Exercise 1.6A

1 Order each set of numbers. Start with the smallest.

   a 3, ‾4, 0, 2, ‾1, ‾3   **b** ‾8, 1, 0, 2, ‾5, ‾1   **c** 0, 1, ‾6, 2, ‾1, 3

   d 3, 0, ‾7, ‾1, 1, ‾2   **e** 5, 0, 1, ‾3, ‾5, 2   **f** 1, ‾9, ‾5, 4, ‾1, 0

2 Order each set of numbers. Start with the smallest.
  Use a number line.

   a 3, ‾1, 0, 2, 6, 1   **b** 2, 0, 3, 6, ‾1, 1   **c** 1, 4, 0, ‾2, ‾1, ‾3

   d 1, ‾11, 9, ‾21, 4, 0   **e** 0, ‾4, 3, ‾5, 5, ‾2   **f** 5, 1, ‾1, ‾9, ‾7, 3

3 List these numbers in order. Start with the smallest.
  Use a number line to help.

   a 2, ‾1, 0, 3, ‾4, 1, ‾5   **b** 0, 3, ‾5, 1, ‾2, ‾4, 5   **c** 6, ‾2, 3, 5, ‾4, 0, ‾7

   d ‾2, ‾1, 0, 3, 2, 4, ‾4   **e** 0, 1, ‾3, 3, ‾2, 7, ‾6   **f** ‾3, 5, ‾2, 1, 4, ‾6, ‾1

Exercise 1.6B

Draw a number line if it helps.

1 Look at this list of numbers: ‾1, 3, 0, ‾2, ‾5, 1, ‾9
  Which of them are smaller than ‾2?

2 Look at this list of numbers: ‾7, ‾12, ‾3, ‾1, 0, ‾2, 5
  Which of them are larger than ‾3?

3 Look at this list of numbers: ‾5, 3, 4, ‾6, ‾1, 0, 1, 2
  Which of them are smaller than ‾1?

4 Look at this list of numbers: 2, ‾4, 1, 0, 3, ‾6, 5, ‾2
  Which of them are larger than ‾2?

5 Look at this list of numbers: 3, ‾3, 0, 1, ‾1, 5, ‾6, 4, ‾5
  a Which of them are larger than ‾3?
  b Which of them are smaller than 3?
  c Which of them are smaller than 0?

1.7 Shifts on a number line

You can use shifts on a number line to calculate with numbers.

Example 1

What number is 5 less than 3?

- Mark 3 on a number line:

- Mark the number 5 smaller than 3:
  This is 5 to the left of 3.

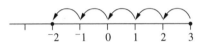

The number that is 5 less than 3 is ⁻2.

5 less than is the same as *5 smaller than*

Exercise 1.7A

1 Use a number line to find the number that is:

    a 4 less than 1   **b** 3 less than ⁻1
    c 8 less than 4   **d** 9 less than ⁻2
    e 7 less than 2   **f** 6 less than ⁻5
    g 11 less than 10   **h** 12 less than ⁻3
    i 10 less than 5   **j** 5 less than ⁻7.

Exercise 1.7B

1 Use a number line to find the number that is:

    a 8 less than 5   **b** 4 less than ⁻1
    c 9 less than 2   **d** 5 less than ⁻2
    e 11 less than 2   **f** 10 less than ⁻5
    g 15 less than 12   **h** 14 less than ⁻1
    i 10 less than 0   **j** 5 less than ⁻5.

You can also find numbers that are larger.

Example 2

What number is 6 more than ‾2?

- Mark ‾2 on a number line:

- Mark the number 6 more than ‾2:
  This is 6 to the right of ‾2.

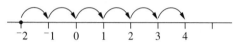

The number that is 6 more than ‾2 is 4.

> *6 more than* is the same
> as *6 larger than*

Exercise 1.7C _____

1 What number is:

a	5 more than ‾8?	**b**	6 more than ‾1?
c	8 more than ‾3?	**d**	5 more than ‾3?
e	5 more than ‾1?	**f**	4 more than ‾13?
g	9 more than ‾7?	**h**	4 more than ‾4?
i	7 more than ‾8?	**j**	11 more than ‾5?

Exercise 1.7D _____

1 What number is:

a	5 more than ‾4?	**b**	6 more than ‾3?
c	8 more than ‾6?	**d**	5 more than ‾5?
e	5 more than ‾7?	**f**	4 more than ‾14?
g	9 more than ‾17?	**h**	4 more than ‾1?
i	7 more than ‾18?	**j**	11 more than ‾10?

▶ You can add or subtract numbers using shifts on a number line.

- You *add* by shifting to the *right*.

  To work out: ‾4 + 9
  Think of this as: start at ‾4 and shift 9 *to the right*.

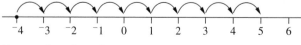

  So   ‾4 + 9 = 5

- You subtract by shifting to the *left*.

  To work out: $^-4 - 9$

  Think of this as: start at $^-4$ and shift 9 *to the left*.

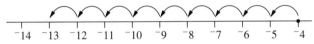

$^-14$	$^-13$	$^-12$	$^-11$	$^-10$	$^-9$	$^-8$	$^-7$	$^-6$	$^-5$	$^-4$

  So $^-4 - 9 = {}^-13$

Exercise 1.7E

1 Copy and complete:

   a $^-6 + 9 =$ **b** $^-8 + 12 =$

   c $^-3 + 7 =$ **d** $^-11 + 9 =$

   e $^-9 + 5 =$ **f** $^-12 + 17 =$

   g $^-12 + 15 =$ **h** $^-11 + 14 =$

   i $^-15 + 17 =$ **j** $^-14 + 14 =$

   k $^-12 + 17 =$ **l** $^-14 + 18 =$

2 **a** $5 - 9 =$ **b** $7 - 12 =$

   c $12 - 15 =$ **d** $11 - 15 =$

   e $^-2 - 9 =$ **f** $^-5 - 8 =$

   g $^-9 - 2 =$ **h** $^-14 - 15 =$

   i $3 - 24 =$ **j** $^-1 - 15 =$

   k $17 - 25 =$ **l** $21 - 50 =$

Exercise 1.7F

1 Shift both ways (*left to subtract* and *right to add*) in these.
Using a number line to help, copy and complete:

   a $^-6 + 3 + 1 =$ **b** $5 - 8 + 1 =$

   c $^-7 + 5 - 4 =$ **d** $^-12 - 3 + 10 =$

   e $3 - 10 + 4 =$ **f** $^-3 + 2 - 4 =$

   g $^-5 + 7 - 12 =$ **h** $^-4 - 8 + 12 =$

   i $^-3 + 5 - 8 =$ **j** $12 - 15 - 8 =$

   k $^-7 + 2 - 8 =$ **l** $^-1 - 8 + 15 =$

2 **a** $^-3 - 4 - 7 =$ **b** $2 - 9 - 5 =$

   c $7 - 5 + 3 =$ **d** $4 - 8 - 5 =$

   e $^-6 - 3 + 2 =$ **f** $18 - 5 + 3 =$

   g $^-7 + 5 - 3 =$ **h** $^-10 - 6 + 14 =$

   i $^-6 - 5 + 13 =$ **j** $2 - 7 - 14 =$

   k $^-5 - 8 + 20 =$ **l** $^-4 + 17 - 5 =$

1.8 Solving problems with negative numbers

Example

At noon the temperature was 8 °C.
By 10 pm the temperature had fallen by 12°.
What was the temperature at 10 pm?

You can think of this as a vertical number line.
See it as a thermometer.

Starting at 8 °C, a fall of 12° is: $8 - 12 = {}^-4$

So, the temperature at 10 pm was ${}^-4$ °C.

Exercise 1.8A

1 The temperature at 10 am was 11 °C.
   By 11 pm the temperature had fallen by 17°.
   What was the temperature at 11 pm?

2 Frozen foods needs to be kept at ${}^-4$ °C.
   Mike keeps his freezers 3° lower than this.
   At what temperature does Mike keep his freezers?

3 Jaz has £42 in her bank account. She buys:

a bag for	£12
a pair of shoes for	£20
a body warmer for	£18

   A week later she goes to the cash machine.
   What will the machine show the account stands at?

4 At high tide 2 metres of a boat is above the sea wall.
   The tide falls by 5 metres.

   Ravi says the height above the wall now is ${}^-3$ metres.
   Draw a diagram to show what Ravi means.

5 In a chill box the temperature was 3 °C.
   This table shows changes over the next four hours.

After	Change in temp
1 hour	fall of 6°
2 hours	rise of 2°
3 hours	rise of 3°
4 hours	fall of 4°

   After 4 hours what was the temperature in the box?

Exercise 1.8B

1 Dave started the week with £6 in cash.
   At the end of the week Dave said he had ⁻£2.50 in cash.
   How much cash did Dave spend in the week?
   Explain how you worked it out.

2 At 3 pm the temperature was 5 °C.
   By 2 am the next day there was a fall in temperature of
   11 °. What was the temperature at 2 am?

3 At 4 am the wind chill was ⁻14 °C. By 6 am there was a
   rise of 5 °. Find the wind chill at 6 am.

4 You have £35 in the bank. You earn £14 and spend £66.
   How much does the cash machine say you now have?

1.9 Factors

Some divisions have whole number answers.
Some divisions leave a remainder.

Example 1

Calculate $36 \div 4$

$\qquad 36 \div 4 = 9$

You say that 36 can be divided exactly by 4.

Example 2

Calculate $36 \div 5$

$\qquad 36 \div 5 = 7$ remainder 1

You say that 36 cannot be divided exactly by 5 as there is a
remainder of 1.

Exercise 1.9A

1 Calculate each of these, giving the remainder where appropriate.
     a $45 \div 9$ b $56 \div 8$ c $63 \div 8$ d $38 \div 4$ e $44 \div 3$ f $96 \div 4$
     g $65 \div 5$ h $28 \div 3$ i $48 \div 5$ j $96 \div 12$ k $30 \div 4$ l $60 \div 7$

Exercise 1.9B

1 Which numbers between 50 and 60 can be divided exactly
   by 3?

2 I think of a number.
It is between 10 and 20.
When I divide the number by 7 I get a remainder of 1.
What is the number?

▶ The **factors** of a number are whole numbers that divide exactly into it.

For example:

The **factors** of 20 are: 1, 2, 4, 5, 10, 20   (they all divide exactly into 20)
The **factors** of 35 are: 1, 5, 7, 35   (they all divide exactly into 35)

Exercise 1.9C

1 List all the factors of:

a 8	**b** 15	**c** 18	**d** 11
e 12	**f** 16	**g** 10	**h** 19

2 Copy and fill in this table.

Number	Factors
21	
22	
23	
24	
25	
26	
27	
28	
29	
30	

3 Three of the factors of 100 are 1, 25 and 50.
What are the other factors of 100?

4 a Which numbers in this list are not factors of 60?

    3   25   12   18   5   6   20   15   4   8   30

  b Say why they are not factors.

Exercise 1.9D

1 List all the factors of:

a 40	**b** 72	**c** 64
d 90	**e** 120	**f** 51

2 Which numbers between 30 and 50 have 8 as a factor?

3 What factors of 42 are also factors of 54?

4 Which has most factors, 75 or 76? Explain your answer.

5 Which factors of 30 are also factors of 45?

___

1.10 Multiples

Sometimes it is quicker to multiply two numbers mentally than by using a calculator.

Exercise 1.10A ___

1 Calculate each of these.
   Do not use a calculator.

    a 9×7 **b** 15×4 **c** 12×7
    d 19×6 **e** 7×6 **f** $3 \times 4 \times 5$
    g 9×18 **h** 21×7 **i** 36×8
    j 14×9

Exercise 1.10B ___

1 Write down 3 different multiplications that each have an answer of 24.

2 Write down a different multiplication that has the same answer as 15×6.

▶ Factors and multiples are linked:
   you know that 3 is a factor of 15, so 15 must be a **multiple** of 3.

    6, 9, 12, 15, 18, 21, 24, 27, 30, 33, 36, 39, 42, ..., ... are all **multiples** of 3.

      6 is the 2nd multiple of 3
      9 is the 3rd multiple of 3
    12 is the 4th multiple of 3
    15 is the 5th multiple of 3
     •   •   •   •
     •   •   •   •
    60 is the 20th multiple of 3

Exercise 1.10C

1 a What is the 6th multiple of 8?
   b Find the 9th multiple of 7.
   c Find the 8th multiple of 3.
   d Give the 5th multiple of 7.
   e What is the 7th multiple of 12?

2 a Which of these is a multiple of 2?   3, 4, 5, 6, 7, 8, 9, 20, 25, 30, 44, 55
   b Which of these is a multiple of 5?   20, 24, 35, 50, 64, 72, 90, 1155
   c Which of these is a multiple of 6?   26, 30, 32, 42, 56
   d Which of these is a multiple of 9?   19, 24, 27, 45, 56, 63
   e Which of these is a multiple of 12?   62, 72, 108, 168, 180, 220

3 a List the first eight multiples of 7.
   b List the first six multiples of 4.
   c Which number between 20 and 40 is a multiple of 4 and 7?

4 List all the numbers less than 50 that are multiples of 3 and 5.

5 a 24 is a multiple of which numbers?
   b 40 is a multiple of which numbers?

Exercise 1.10D

1 Copy and complete:

      56 is the ☐ th multiple of 8.

      56 is the ☐ th multiple of 7.

      56 is the 4th multiple of ☐.

2 Add the seventh multiple of 8 to the fifteenth multiple of 4.

3 Take the sixth multiple of 7 from the tenth multiple of 12.

4 What numbers between 50 and 70 are multiples of 4?

5 What numbers between 70 and 100 are multiples of 8?

6 These are the ages of three people.

      Tom's age is the 9th multiple of 3.
      Rina's age is the 4th multiple of 9.
      Tina's age is the 5th multiple of 6.

   a Who is the oldest?
   b Who is the youngest?
   c List them in age order, youngest first.
   d Find the total of their ages.

7 The lottery 'bonus ball' was the 7th multiple of 6.
What number was this 'bonus ball'.

8 The number of Ali's house was the 12th multiple of 15.
What was the number of Ali's house?

1.11 Prime numbers

Prime numbers are numbers which have only two different factors, 1 and the number itself.
The first four prime numbers are: 2   (factors 1 and 2)
3   (factors 1 and 3)
5   (factors 1 and 5)
7   (factors 1 and 7)

> 1 is *not* a prime number as it has only one factor.

The next prime number *is not* 9 because the factors of 9 are 1, 3, and 9.   So, 9 has three factors.

Exercise 1.11A

1 List the prime numbers between 10 and 20.

2 Is 27 a prime number? Explain your answer.

3 What prime number is closest to 40?

4 What is the 10th prime number? (2 is the first.)

5 There are two prime numbers between 50 and 60.
What are they?

6 List the numbers 90 to 100. Which are prime?

> To make sure a number is prime, list its factors. If you can find more than two factors the number is *not* prime.

Exercise 1.11B

1 List all the prime numbers between 50 and 90.

2 Explain why 39 is not a prime number.

3 Add all the prime numbers less than 20.

4 Find the next prime number after 67.

5 Are all prime numbers odd? Explain.

6 List the numbers from 70 to 80. Which are prime?

1.12 Square numbers

▶ To make a **square** number you multiply a number by itself.
25 is a square number because $5 \times 5 = \mathbf{25}$
The first square number is $1 \times 1 = 1$

Note:
1×1 is not equal to 2.

▶ You write 6^2, 'six squared', to mean 6×6.

Example

Find the value of 10^2 (ten squared).

$$10^2 = 10 \times 10 = \mathbf{100}$$

Hint: 100 is a square number and you can make a square with 100 dots. The square will be 10 dots by 10 dots.

Exercise 1.12A

1 What is the value of 6^2?

2 Calculate the value of 'three squared'.

3 **a** What does 7^2 mean?
b What is the value of 7^2?

4 Calculate the value of each of these:
a 4^2 **b** 8^2 **c** 9^2 **d** 12^2 **e** 20^2

5 Calculate the value of each of these:
a 15^2 **b** 16^2 **c** 70^2 **d** 50^2 **e** 11^2

6 List the first ten square numbers.

7 What square number is closest to 150?

Exercise 1.12B

1 What is 14^2?

2 Calculate the value of each of these:
a 25^2 **b** 19^2 **c** 56^2 **d** 0^2 **e** 21^2

3 List all the square numbers between 120 and 150.

4 What square number is closest to 300?

5 Calculate the value of each of these:

a $4^2 + 5^2$ **b** $7^2 + 4^2$ **c** $8^2 - 16^2$

d $4^2 \times 2^2$ **e** $3^2 + 5^2 + 6^2$ **f** $100^2 - 10^2$

6 What is the missing number? $3^2 + 4^2 = \boxed{}$

1.13 Finding square roots

▶ Finding the **square root** is the opposite of finding a square.

Example

Find the square root of 64.

     $64 = 8 \times 8$ so **8** is the square root of 64.

▶ You write **the square root of 64** like this $\sqrt{64}$.

▶ You can find the square root of a number in several ways:

   1 by inspection when you can see the answer.

     Example   Find $\sqrt{36}$ Answer $= 6$

   2 with a calculator

     Example   Find $\sqrt{3136}$

         Press

         so $\sqrt{3136} = 56$

> **Hint:**
> You should be able to see that $6 \times 6 = 36$

Exercise 1.13A _____

1 Find each of these square roots by inspection.

   a $\sqrt{25}$ **b** $\sqrt{9}$ **c** $\sqrt{81}$ **d** $\sqrt{49}$ **e** $\sqrt{100}$ **f** $\sqrt{144}$

   g $\sqrt{4}$ **h** $\sqrt{121}$ **i** $\sqrt{169}$ **j** $\sqrt{16}$ **k** $\sqrt{400}$ **l** $\sqrt{1}$

2 Use a calculator to find these square roots.

   a $\sqrt{289}$ **b** $\sqrt{1849}$ **c** $\sqrt{80\,656}$ **d** $\sqrt{15\,129}$

   e $\sqrt{1936}$ **f** $\sqrt{14\,641}$ **g** $\sqrt{44\,944}$ **h** $\sqrt{54\,756}$

3 Find $\sqrt{400} + \sqrt{49}$.

Exercise 1.13B

1 Find $\sqrt{64} + \sqrt{100} - \sqrt{25}$

2 Use a calculator to work out:

   a $\sqrt{324}$ **b** $\sqrt{576}$ **c** $\sqrt{1225}$

   d $\sqrt{4356}$ **e** $\sqrt{2401}$ **f** $\sqrt{6241}$

   g $\sqrt{7744}$ **h** $\sqrt{10\,816}$ **i** $\sqrt{15\,376}$

3 a Find $\sqrt{256}$ with your calculator.
   b Square the answer you get. What do you discover?

4 Copy and complete:

   a $\sqrt{1296} + \sqrt{49} =$

   b $\sqrt{729} - \sqrt{100} =$

   c $\sqrt{2209} + \sqrt{9} =$

   d $\sqrt{16} + \sqrt{1681} =$

   e $\sqrt{81} + \sqrt{100} - \sqrt{25} - \sqrt{9} =$

1.14 Sequences from patterns

▶ A **sequence** is a set of numbers linked by a rule.
For example the sequence of even numbers is 2, 4, 6, 8, 10, ...
A rule for this sequence is 'start at 2 and add 2 each time'.

▶ A **term** is a number in the sequence.
For example in the even number sequence: 2, 4, 6, 8, ...
term 1 is   2
term 2 is   4
term 3 is   6
and so on ...

▶ This is the sequence of **square numbers**.

and so on ...

▶ This is the sequence of **triangle numbers**.

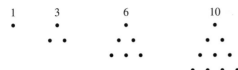

and so on ...

Exercise 1.14A

1 **a** List the sequence of the first ten odd numbers.
What are these terms in the sequence:
b Term 3?
c Term 5?
d Term 9?
e Find Term 15 of the sequence.

2 Give these terms from the even number sequence:
a Term 4   **b** Term 12   **c** Term 27

3 Copy the square numbers sequence.
a Draw the next three patterns.
b What is Term 7 of the square numbers sequence?

4 Give these terms of the square numbers sequence:
a Term 8   **b** Term 9   **c** Term 10

5 **a** Draw Pattern 5 in the triangle numbers sequence.
b How many dots are in Pattern 5?

6 **a** Draw Pattern 6 in the triangle numbers sequence.
b How many dots are in Pattern 6?

7 How many dots are in Pattern 7 of triangle numbers?

8 Look at this sequence of patterns.

Pattern 1   Pattern 2   Pattern 3

a Draw Pattern 5 in the sequence.
b How many matches will be in Pattern 6?
c How many matches will be in Pattern 10?

Exercise 1.14B

1 **a** Draw Pattern 9 in the square number sequence.
   b How many dots has this pattern?

2 **a** Draw Patterns 8 and 9 in the triangle number sequence.
   b List the first ten triangle numbers.

3 This shows a sequence of paving stones.

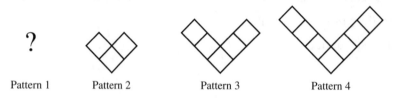

Pattern 1   Pattern 2   Pattern 3   Pattern 4

   a Draw Pattern 1.
   b Draw the next two patterns in the sequence.
   c Find the number of stones in Pattern 8.

4 Paving stones are put around flower beds in a sequence.

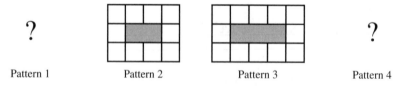

Pattern 1   Pattern 2   Pattern 3   Pattern 4

   a Draw Patterns 1 and 4.
   b List the first six terms in this sequence.
   c How many stones would be in Pattern 10?
      Show your working.

1.15 Number sequences

▶ You can describe a number sequence in words.

Example

Describe the sequence 5, 8, 11, 14, …, …, …
It starts at 5 and you add 3 each time.

Exercise 1.15A

1 Copy each sequence and write the next two terms.
   Then say how it continues.

   a 10, 12, 14, 16, 18, . . .   **b** 6, 9, 12, 15, 18, . . .
   c 3, 6, 12, 24, 48, 96, . . .   **d** 100, 98, 96, 94, 92, . . .
   e 1, 3, 9, 27, 81, . . .   **f** 5, 10, 15, 20, 25, . . .
   g 1000, 500, 250, . . .   **h** 6, 13, 20, 27, . . .

2 Copy each sequence then use the rule to write the next
   three terms.

Sequence	**Rule**
a 6, 24, . . . , . . . , . . .	Add 18.
b 200, 188, . . . , . . . , . . .	Subtract 12.
c 256, . . . , . . . , . . .	Divide by 2.
d 5, . . . , . . . , . . .	Double then add 1.

Exercise 1.15B

1 Describe each of these sequence in words:

   a 17, 12, 7, 2, ⁻3, . . .   **b** 18, 32, 46, 60, . . .
   c 256, 128, 64, 32, . . .   **d** 10, 100, 1000, . . .
   e 3, 7, 11, 15, . . .   **f** 125, 109, 93, . . .

2 Copy each sequence in question **1** and write the next two terms.

3 Copy each sequence then use the rule to write the next
   three terms.

Sequence	**Rule**
a 2, . . . , . . . , . . .	Double then add 3.
b 2, . . . , . . . , . . .	Multiply by 4 then subtract 5.
c 65 536, . . . , . . . , . . .	Subtract 50.
d 416, . . . , . . . , . . .	Half it.
e 3, 7, . . .	Multiply by 5 then subtract 8.

4 A sequence starts 1, 5, . . .

   a Give two different rules it could be using.
   b For each rule write the first five terms in the sequence.

5 Write a rule for a sequence.
   Use your rule to write the next three terms in these sequences:

   a 2, . . . , . . . , . . .   **b** 5, . . . , . . . , . . .   **c** 8, . . . , . . . , . . .

1.16 Fractions

A fraction shows how something is divided up or shared out.

A fraction we use often is $\frac{1}{2}$.

We are used to dividing in half or into two parts.

Each part is $\frac{1}{2}$.

We can show quarters in the same way.

$\frac{1}{4}$

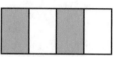

Each part is $\frac{1}{4}$.

$\frac{3}{4}$

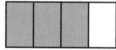

Each part is $\frac{1}{4}$.

You can show thirds on a diagram like this:
Each part is $\frac{1}{3}$.

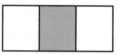

You can show fifths on a diagram like this:
Each part is $\frac{1}{5}$.

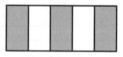

You can show eighths on a diagram like this:
Each part is $\frac{1}{8}$.

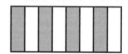

You can show tenths on a diagram like this:
Each part is $\frac{1}{10}$.

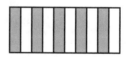

Exercise 1.16A _____

1 Draw diagrams to show these fractions:

   a $\frac{2}{3}$ **b** $\frac{4}{4}$ **c** $\frac{3}{8}$ **d** $\frac{7}{10}$ **e** $\frac{5}{8}$ **f** $\frac{3}{10}$

2 What fraction is shown by each of these?

   a    **b**    **c**

Exercise 1.16B

1 Draw diagrams to show these fractions:

    a $\frac{7}{8}$ b $\frac{2}{5}$ c $\frac{9}{10}$ d $\frac{2}{8}$ e $\frac{6}{10}$ f $\frac{3}{5}$

2 What fraction is shown by each of these?

    a   b 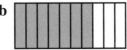   c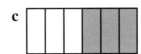

You can compare fractions with this type of diagram, but the diagrams must be the same size.

Example

Which is larger, $\frac{2}{3}$ or $\frac{3}{4}$?

- Draw and shade a diagram for $\frac{2}{3}$.

- Draw and shade a diagram for $\frac{3}{4}$.

Compare the shaded parts: $\frac{3}{4}$ is larger than $\frac{2}{3}$.

Exercise 1.16C

1 a Draw diagrams to show $\frac{2}{3}$ and $\frac{7}{8}$.

   b Which is larger, $\frac{2}{3}$ or $\frac{7}{8}$?

2 a Draw diagrams to show $\frac{3}{10}$ and $\frac{2}{5}$.

   b Which is smaller, $\frac{3}{10}$ or $\frac{2}{5}$?

3 a Draw diagrams to show $\frac{1}{3}$ and $\frac{2}{8}$.

   b Which is smaller, $\frac{1}{3}$ or $\frac{2}{8}$?

Exercise 1.16D

1 a Draw diagrams to compare $\frac{1}{3}$, $\frac{2}{5}$ and $\frac{3}{10}$.

   b Which is the smallest?

   c Which is the largest?

2 a Draw diagrams to compare $\frac{3}{4}$, $\frac{5}{8}$, $\frac{9}{10}$ and $\frac{4}{5}$.

   b List the fractions in order. Start with the smallest.

1.17 Simplifying fractions

You can simplify a fraction by cancelling.
You need to find a number that divides exactly into both
parts of the fraction.

> **Remember:**
> The two parts of a
> fraction are the
> numerator 'at the top'
> and denominator 'down
> below'.

Example

Simplify $\frac{15}{25}$.

15 and 25 both divide exactly by 5

So, divide both parts by 5:

$$\frac{15}{25} = \frac{3}{5}$$

Exercise 1.17A

1 Simplify each of these fractions.

    a $\frac{15}{35}$ **b** $\frac{18}{21}$ **c** $\frac{14}{49}$ **d** $\frac{11}{55}$ **e** $\frac{15}{21}$

    f $\frac{12}{45}$ **g** $\frac{21}{56}$ **h** $\frac{12}{27}$ **i** $\frac{10}{65}$ **j** $\frac{21}{30}$

Exercise 1.17B

1 Simplify each of these fractions.

    a $\frac{21}{35}$ **b** $\frac{25}{85}$ **c** $\frac{3}{81}$ **d** $\frac{35}{56}$ **e** $\frac{12}{51}$

    f $\frac{35}{80}$ **g** $\frac{49}{84}$ **h** $\frac{9}{42}$ **i** $\frac{66}{165}$ **j** $\frac{28}{77}$

1.18 Lowest terms

A fraction is in its lowest terms when:

    you cannot find a number that divides exactly into both parts,

or   it will not cancel down any more.

Example

Simplify $\frac{24}{64}$ to its lowest terms.

Divide both parts by 4: $\overset{\div 4}{\overbrace{\frac{24}{64}}_{\div 4}} = \frac{6}{16}$ but 6 and 16 divide by 2.

Divide both parts by 2: $\overset{\div 2}{\overbrace{\frac{6}{16}}_{\div 2}} = \frac{3}{8}$

$\frac{3}{8}$ will not cancel any more.

Now 3 and 8 cannot be divided.

In its lowest terms: $\frac{24}{64} = \frac{3}{8}$

Exercise 1.18A

1 Simplify each of these fractions to its lowest terms.

a $\frac{24}{40}$ b $\frac{18}{81}$ c $\frac{12}{32}$ d $\frac{28}{70}$ e $\frac{24}{36}$

f $\frac{30}{70}$ g $\frac{32}{48}$ h $\frac{36}{60}$ i $\frac{20}{80}$ j $\frac{16}{56}$

When you cannot cancel any more, a fraction is in its **lowest terms**.

Exercise 1.18B

1 Simplify each of these fractions to its lowest terms.

a $\frac{24}{60}$ b $\frac{32}{72}$ c $\frac{27}{90}$ d $\frac{36}{84}$ e $\frac{45}{60}$

f $\frac{40}{100}$ g $\frac{48}{144}$ h $\frac{56}{60}$ i $\frac{12}{100}$ j $\frac{48}{156}$

1.19 Equivalent fractions

Equivalent fractions use different numbers but they have the same value.
To make equivalent fractions you multiply both parts of a fraction by the same number.

Example

Give three different fractions equivalent to $\frac{3}{5}$.

• multiply both parts by 3 $\frac{3\times3}{5\times3} = \frac{9}{15}$

• multiply both parts by 4 $\frac{3\times4}{5\times4} = \frac{12}{20}$

• multiply both parts by 9 $\frac{3\times9}{5\times9} = \frac{27}{45}$

So: $\frac{9}{15}$, $\frac{12}{20}$, and $\frac{27}{45}$ are equivalent to $\frac{3}{5}$.

Exercise 1.19A _____

1 Find three different fractions equivalent to:

    a $\frac{1}{4}$ **b** $\frac{2}{5}$ **c** $\frac{5}{8}$ **d** $\frac{4}{7}$ **e** $\frac{1}{2}$

2 Find three fractions equivalent to each of these:

    a $\frac{3}{5}$ **b** $\frac{7}{10}$ **c** $\frac{7}{12}$ **d** $\frac{9}{50}$ **e** $\frac{3}{100}$

3 Are $\frac{6}{8}$ and $\frac{18}{24}$ equivalent?
   Explain your answer.

Exercise 1.19B _____

1 Find three different fractions equivalent to:

    a $\frac{3}{4}$ **b** $\frac{4}{5}$ **c** $\frac{7}{8}$ **d** $\frac{3}{7}$

2 Write three equivalent fractions for each of:

    a $\frac{5}{9}$ **b** $\frac{5}{6}$ **c** $\frac{7}{40}$ **d** $\frac{7}{11}$

3 Show how $\frac{5}{9}$ and $\frac{20}{36}$ are equivalent.

4 Copy and complete these equivalent fractions.

    a $\frac{3}{4} = \frac{\square}{28}$ **b** $\frac{5}{8} = \frac{25}{\square}$ **c** $\frac{2}{3} = \frac{\square}{21}$ **d** $\frac{1}{5} = \frac{6}{\square}$

5 Copy and complete these equivalent fractions.

    a $\frac{\square}{5} = \frac{12}{20}$ **b** $\frac{3}{\square} = \frac{21}{35}$ **c** $\frac{\square}{7} = \frac{30}{42}$ **d** $\frac{5}{\square} = \frac{25}{60}$

1.20 Decimal place value

▶ A decimal number has two parts:

          3.67

    whole   decimal part
    number part

   You say: three point six seven (*not* sixty seven)

▶ You can use a decimal value diagram to
see the value of each digit:

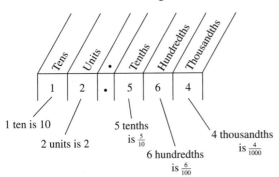

Exercise 1.20A

1 What does each underlined digit stand for?

   a 3.2<u>8</u>1   **b** 163.<u>5</u>32   **c** 0.00<u>6</u>   **d** 12.5<u>6</u>3
   e 1.09<u>5</u>   **f** 173.<u>2</u>96   **g** 60.3<u>7</u>2   **h** 125.05<u>8</u>
   i 0.7<u>1</u>8   **j** 3030.<u>6</u>14   **k** 1.08<u>5</u>   **l** 111.1<u>1</u>1

2 The missing digits in the number 3.☐☐☐ are:

   a 4 that stands for $\frac{4}{1000}$
   a 2 that stands for $\frac{2}{10}$
   and a 7 that stands for $\frac{7}{100}$
   Write the number in full.

3 The missing digits in the number 152.☐☐☐ are:

   a 6 that stands for $\frac{6}{100}$
   a 3 that stands for $\frac{3}{10}$
   and a 1 that stands for $\frac{1}{1000}$
   Write the number in full.

Exercise 1.20B

1 What does each underlined digit stand for?

   a 5.3<u>4</u>5   **b** 1.<u>8</u>07   **c** 9.12<u>5</u>   **d** 12.<u>3</u>06   **e** 17.4<u>5</u>
   f 6.<u>2</u>   **g** 6.01<u>8</u>   **h** 1.0<u>6</u>5   **i** 5.2<u>5</u>6

2 The missing digits in the number 362.☐3☐ are:

   a 2 that stands for $\frac{2}{1000}$
   and a 5 that stands for $\frac{5}{10}$.
   Write the number in full.

3 In each number there are missing digits.
The missing digits are:
a 4 that stands for $\frac{4}{1000}$, a 7 that stands for $\frac{7}{10}$
and a 3 that stands for $\frac{3}{100}$.
Write each number in full.

a 37.2☐☐   **b** 152.☐8☐   **c** 0.☐☐1   **d** 105.☐0☐   **e** 66.☐☐4
f 53.2☐   **g** 1.☐2   **h** 27.☐☐   **i** 1856.0☐3   **j** 47.☐☐3
k 0.0☐   **l** 0.00☐   **m** 3.☐☐☐   **n** 5.☐1   **o** 3.☐0☐

4 What number is $\frac{4}{100}$ more than 21.635?

5 What number is $\frac{3}{1000}$ less than 16.086?

6 What number is $\frac{7}{10}$ more than 2.56?

1.21 Ordering decimals

▶ To order decimals:
  • put the decimal points underneath each other.
  • fill any empty place on the right with zeros.
  • arrange the numbers in order. Start with the units,
    then the tenths, hundredths and so on.

Example

Put these decimals in order, smallest first.

    0.26   1.574   0.045   6   0.58   0.273

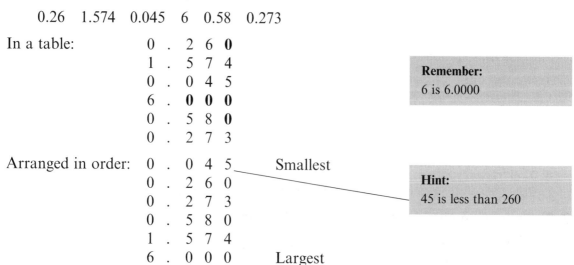

In a table:
    0 . 2 6 **0**
    1 . 5 7 4
    0 . 0 4 5
    6 . **0 0 0**
    0 . 5 8 **0**
    0 . 2 7 3

Remember:
6 is 6.0000

Arranged in order: 0 . 0 4 5 ——— Smallest
    0 . 2 6 0
    0 . 2 7 3
    0 . 5 8 0
    1 . 5 7 4
    6 . 0 0 0   Largest

Hint:
45 is less than 260

So, in order, the numbers are: 0.045, 0.26, 0.273, 0.58, 1.574, 6.58

Exercise 1.21A _____

1 Which is the larger number?

   a 0.45 or 0.405   **b** 1.623 or 1.7   **c** 1.08 or 1.121
   d 0.004 or 0.011   **e** 0.109 or 0.12   **f** 2.44 or 2.428

2 Make the smallest decimal number possible from
   9, 0, ., 0 and 7.

3 Make the largest number you can from 4, ., 0, 5 and 3.

4 Put these in order, smallest first: 0.6, 0.284, 0.46, 0.528

5 Put these in order, largest first: 1.062, 0.192, 0.02, 0.3,
   0.104

Exercise 1.21B _____

1 Arrange each set of numbers in order, smallest first.

   a 0.039, 8, 0.27, 0.008, 1.24, 0.092
   b 0.1, 0.09, 0.28, 0.099, 0.042
   c 0.382, 0.19, 0.007, 0.018, 0.77

> If it helps put the
> numbers in a table and
> then order them.

2 Eight pieces of wood have these lengths:

   0.12 m, 4 m, 0.035 m, 2.76 m, 0.3 m, 0.074 m, 1.3 m, 0.009 m

   Arrange these lengths from longest to shortest.

3 Which widths of letters will pass through a post box slot
   0.23 m wide?

   0.229 m, 0.30 m, 0.209 m, 0.291 m, 0.199 m, 2.021 m, 0.28 m

4 What number is $\frac{3}{100}$ more than 12.38?

5 The length of a bolt must lie between 0.046 m and
   0.045 m. Which of these lengths fits?

      0.0465 m, 0.0453 m, 0.0462 m, 0.0468 m

1.22 Decimals on a number line

▶ To place a decimal on a number line you must decide
  which numbers it lies between.

Example

Place 3.76 on this number line.

- 3.76 lies between 3.7 and 3.8 so find these on the line.

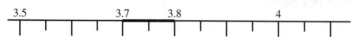

- 3.76 lies between 3.75 and 3.8 so you must estimate.

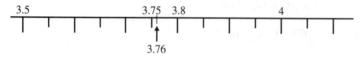

Exercise 1.22A

1 On a copy of the number line above show the positions of:

   a 3.74   **b** 3.98   **c** 3.62

2 On a copy of the number line in question 1 show the position of 4.05

3 On Scale 1 what reading is given by:

   a arrow A   **b** arrow B   **c** arrow C?

Exercise 1.22B

1 Copy Scale 1 without points A, B and C.
   Show the approximate positions of these points.

   a 0.46   **b** 0.40   **c** 0.51   **d** 0.47

2 Draw a number line 10 cm long. Label one end 0.6 and the other 0.7. Show ten divisions between 0.6 and 0.7. On your line indicate the approximate positions of:

   a 0.66   **b** 0.61   **c** 0.69   **d** 0.65

3 Draw a number line 10 cm long. Label one end 0.1 and the other 0.2. Show ten divisions on your line. On your line indicate the approximate positions of:

   a 0.14   **b** 0.16   **c** 0.18   **d** 0.19

1.23 Percentages

▶ A **percentage** is a fraction of 100, so 1% is $\frac{1}{100}$

▶ Some everyday percentages are:

50% which is $\frac{50}{100}$

25% which is $\frac{25}{100}$

75% which is $\frac{75}{100}$

10% which is $\frac{10}{100}$

You could show 32% in this way:

There are 100 squares, and 32 are shaded.
So, 32 of the 100 squares are shaded.
$\frac{32}{100}$ are shaded so, 32% are shaded.

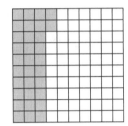

Exercise 1.23A _____

1 What percentage of each square is shaded?

a 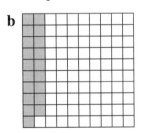   b   c   d

2 What percentage of each square is not shaded?

a 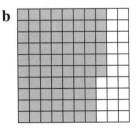   b 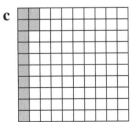   c   d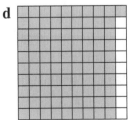

Exercise 1.23B

1 What percentage of each square is shaded?

a 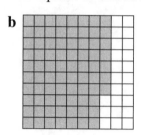 b 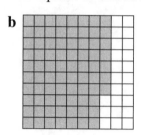 c 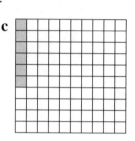 d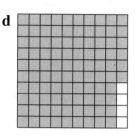

2 Copy and complete for a 100 square:
   a 15% are shaded, so ☐ are not shaded.
   b ☐ are shaded, so 56% are not shaded.
   c 25% are shaded, so ☐ are not shaded.
   d ☐ are shaded, so 32% are not shaded.

1.24 Percentages – the link with fractions and decimals

▶ You know a percentage is a fraction out of 100.
   So 20% means $\frac{20}{100}$ or 20 out of every 100.

▶ Percentages, fractions and decimals are all linked.

Example 1

Show 28% as a fraction and as a decimal.

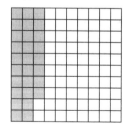 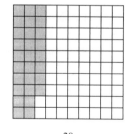 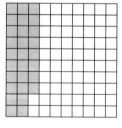

$$28\% \qquad = \qquad \frac{28}{100} \qquad = \qquad 0.28$$

Example 2

Write 70% as a fraction and as a decimal.

$$70\% = \frac{70}{100} = 0.7$$

Remember:
0.7 also means 0.70

Exercise 1.24A

1 Write each of these percentages as a fraction.

  a 35% **b** 17% **c** 95% **d** 6% **e** 50% **f** 60%

2 Write each percentage as a decimal.

  a 54% **b** 75% **c** 12% **d** 25% **e** 40% **f** 80%

3 Write each decimal number as a percentage.

  a 0.63 **b** 0.85 **c** 0.22 **d** 0.3 **e** 0.1 **f** 0.2

Exercise 1.24B

Copy and complete these tables.

1

Percentage	Fraction	Decimal
12%		
		0.36
	$\frac{3}{100}$	
98%		
		0.4
	1	
25%		
	$\frac{9}{100}$	

2

Percentage	Fraction	Decimal
	$\frac{16}{100}$	
57%		
		0.8
	$\frac{6}{100}$	
85%		
		0.15
75%		
		0.77

Revision Exercise 1

Review

1 What is the value of the **bold** digit in each of these numbers?

  a 3686   **b** 50 4**7**2   **c** 6**1**8 281   **d** 30**4** 056

  e 1 **5**65 721 **f** 45 3**6**2   **g** **3** 957 264 **h** 156 3**8**2 675   *Unit 1.1*

2 Think about the number 63 483.

  a What digit is in the hundreds position?

  b What digit is in the ten thousands position?

  c Write the number in words.   *Unit 1.1*

3 Make the largest number you can using all the digits
0, 3, 5, 7, 8

Review
Unit 1.1

4 Multiply each of these numbers by 10.

a 156	**b** 3047	**c** 26 560	**d** 10 500
e 3342	**f** 56	**g** 1070	**h** 20 547

Unit 1.2

5 There are 1000 metres in one kilometre. How many metres are in:

a 44 km   **b** 1665 km   **c** 1040 km   **d** 5105 km

Unit 1.2

6 Copy and complete this table

Number	÷10	÷1000	÷100
1 650 000			
300 000			
9 080 000			
12 000 000			

Unit 1.3

7 Calculate each of these without a calculator.

a 4×60	**b** 24×80	**c** 68×40	**d** 184×30
e 6×700	**f** 56×700	**g** 28×4000	**h** 121×3000

Unit 1.4

8 Calculate each of these without a calculator.

a $1400 \div 20$	**b** $3600 \div 90$	**c** $15\,000 \div 200$	**d** $2800 \div 70$
e $4200 \div 600$	**f** $180 \div 30$	**g** $15\,000 \div 300$	**h** $5600 \div 80$

Unit 1.4

9 Draw a new number line for each part.
On a number line show all the whole numbers:

a from $^-6$ to 1	**b** from $^-12$ to $^-15$
c from 3 to $^-8$	**d** from 4 to $^-5$
e from $^-10$ to $^-16$	**f** from 0 to $^-7$

Unit 1.5

10 Order each set of numbers. Start with the smallest.

a $^-2$, 0, 3, $^-4$, 4, 1	**b** 3, 2, 0, 1, $^-4$
c 4, $^-2$, 1, $^-3$, $^-5$, 2	**d** 6, $^-2$, $^-5$, 1, 0, 3

Unit 1.6

11 Which of these numbers is smaller than $^-3$?
5, 4, $^-2$, 1, 0, $^-6$, $^-8$, $^-5$, 3, 2

Unit 1.6

12 Find the number that is:

a 9 less than 4	**b** 3 less than $^-5$	**c** 7 less than $^-2$
d 4 more than $^-3$	**e** 8 more than $^-2$	**f** 12 less than 5

Unit 1.7

13 Copy and complete each of these. *Review*
  a $^-5+3+4=$ **b** $6-9+1=$ **c** $^-6+3-8=$
  d $^-5+4+2-6=$ **e** $3-9+2+1=$ **f** $^-10+4-3+8=$ *Unit 1.7*

14 The temperature at 0800 was 13°C.
By 1800 the temperature had fallen by 20 degrees.
What was the temperature at 1800?   *Unit 1.8*

15 The temperature in a chill cabinet was 2°C.
Four hours later the temperature was $^-6$°C.
Calculate this fall in temperature.   *Unit 1.8*

16 Calculate each of these. Give the remainder where appropriate.
  a $56\div4$ **b** $66\div32$ **c** $85\div4$ **d** $120\div5$ **e** $48\div6$ *Unit 1.9*

17 List all the factors of:
  a 24   **b** 30   **c** 56   **d** 80   **e** 96   *Unit 1.9*

18 Calculate each of these, and do not use a calculator.
  a 8×9 **b** 16×5 **c** 12×9 **d** 23×4 **e** 45×7 *Unit 1.10*

19 What is the sixth multiple of eight?   *Unit 1.10*

20 Find the sum of the 3rd multiple of 7 and the 8th multiple of 6.   *Unit 1.10*

21 List all the prime numbers between 10 and 30.   *Unit 1.11*

22 What is the next prime number after 80?   *Unit 1.11*

23 Calculate the value of each of these.
  a 4^2 **b** 6^2 **c** 8^2 **d** 0^2 **e** 12^2 **f** 20^2 *Unit 1.12*

24 List all the square numbers between 50 and 120.   *Unit 1.12*

25 Find each square root by inspection.
  a $\sqrt{81}$ **b** $\sqrt{49}$ **c** $\sqrt{144}$ **d** $\sqrt{64}$ **e** $\sqrt{169}$ *Unit 1.13*

26 Use a calculator to find each of these.
  a $\sqrt{210}$ **b** $\sqrt{265}$ **c** $\sqrt{2468}$ **d** $\sqrt{500}$ **e** $\sqrt{3400}$ *Unit 1.13*

27 List the first 6 terms of the triangle numbers sequence. Show each term as a pattern of dots.

Review

Unit 1.14

28 Copy each sequence and write in the next two terms.

a 9, 13, 17, 21, …, …
b 55, 47, 39, 31, …, …
c 128, 64, 32, …, …
d 147, 144, 141, …, …

Unit 1.15

29 Copy each sequence, then use the rule to write the next 3 terms.

Sequence	Rule
3, …	Double then add 4
5, …	Multiply by 5 then subtract 4
188, …	Subtract 25

Unit 1.15

30 Draw diagrams to show each of these fractions.

a $\frac{3}{5}$ **b** $\frac{5}{8}$ **c** $\frac{7}{10}$ **d** $\frac{3}{4}$

Unit 1.16

31 **a** Draw diagrams to show $\frac{2}{3}$ and $\frac{5}{8}$.
   b Which is larger : $\frac{2}{3}$ or $\frac{5}{8}$?

Unit 1.16

32 Simplify each of these fractions

a $\frac{15}{50}$ **b** $\frac{12}{30}$ **c** $\frac{15}{35}$ **d** $\frac{24}{60}$ **e** $\frac{18}{81}$

Unit 1.17

33 Simplify each of these fractions to its lowest terms.

a $\frac{15}{45}$ **b** $\frac{16}{28}$ **c** $\frac{30}{80}$ **d** $\frac{25}{90}$ **e** $\frac{16}{56}$

Unit 1.18

34 Find three different fractions equivalent to:

a $\frac{3}{5}$ **b** $\frac{3}{4}$ **c** $\frac{5}{8}$ **d** $\frac{7}{10}$ **e** $\frac{1}{4}$

Unit 1.19

35 Give the value of each **bold** digit.

a 12.1**6**5   **b** 148.0**6**6   **c** 30.10**2**5   **d** 177.3**8**8
e 135.62**5**6   **f** 404.2**5**82   **g** 175.0**5**58   **h** 0.0**5**6753

Unit 1.20

36 What number is $\frac{3}{100}$ more than 25.545?

Unit 1.20

37 Put each set of numbers in order, smallest first.

a 1.15, 2.004, 1.85, 2.4, 1.6, 2.44
b 0.4, 0.15, 0.6, 0.23, 0.3, 0.401, 0.2

Unit 1.21

38 Draw a number line to show values between 3 and 4.
Show these numbers on the number line.

   a 3.6   **b** 3.24   **c** 3.72   **d** 3.9   *Unit 1.22*

39 26% of a square is shaded.
What percentage of the square is not shaded?   *Unit 1.23*

40 Write each of these percentages as a fraction.

   a 45%   **b** 70%   **c** 18%   **d** 32%   **e** 8%   *Unit 1.24*

41 Write each percentage as a decimal.

   a 28%   **b** 35%   **c** 64%   **d** 85%   **e** 4%   *Unit 1.24*

42 Write each decimal number as a percentage.

   a 0.72   **b** 0.56   **c** 0.28   **d** 0.08   **e** 0.01   *Unit 1.24*

43 Which is larger: 0.65 or 62%?   *Unit 1.24*

44 What value is 10% more than 0.34?   *Unit 1.24*

2 NUMBER CALCULATIONS

2.1 Rounding to the nearest 10, 100, 1000, ...

▶ To round a number to the nearest 10 look at the digit in the units position.
If it is 5 or above then round up the tens digit.

Example 1

Round 1647 to the nearest 10.   1647 ◄─────────────── Yes! 5 or above.
So round **up** the tens
digit from 4 to 5.

So 1647 rounded to the nearest 10 is **1650**.

Example 2

Round 2854 to the nearest 10.
Round down to **2850** (since 4 is less than 5).

▶ To round a number to the nearest 100 look at the digit in the tens position.

Example 3

Round 12 846 to the nearest 100.   12 846 ◄─────────────── No! less than 5
So round **down** to 8.

This gives **12 800**.

▶ To round to the nearest 1000 look at the digit in the hundreds position.

Exercise 2.1A _____

1 Round each number to the nearest 10.
   a 124   **b** 156   **c** 638   **d** 54   **e** 1735

2 Round each number to the nearest 100.
   a 7364   **b** 8339   **c** 18 308   **d** 869

3 Round each number to the nearest 1000.
   a 1638   **b** 7288   **c** 12 975   **d** 65 395

4 Round 127 484 to:
   a the nearest 10
   b the nearest 100
   c the nearest 1000

5 Round 299 502 to the nearest thousand.

Exercise 2.1B

1 What is 77 rounded to the nearest 100?

2 **a** Round 12 999 to the nearest 10, 100 and 1000.
   b What do you notice?

3 A number is rounded to the nearest 10 and the answer is
   120.
   a What is the largest number it could be?
   b What is the smallest number it could be?

4 Rounded to the nearest thousand, the number of trees in
   a park is 12 000. What is the largest number of trees there
   could be in the park?

5 Write three numbers that will all be 19 000 when they are
   rounded to the nearest 1000.

2.2 Estimating answers

You can estimate answers by rounding before you calculate.

- Estimating is a mental calculation you can do quickly
  and easily.
- Decide for yourself how you are going to round the
  numbers.

Estimating is probably a
mental calculation. It is a
way to check that the
answer you work out is
about the right size.

Example 1

Estimate 37×62

To estimate the answer: round 37 up to 40, and 62 down to 60.
Now calculate mentally $40 \times 60 = 2400$

So   as an estimate 37×62 is about 2400
        (You can write this as $37 \times 62 \approx 2400$)

The symbol $\approx$ means
approximately equal to.

Example 2

Estimate $3742 + 688 + 235 - 573$

Calculate mentally: $3750 + 700 + 250 - 550$

So   as an estimate $374 + 688 + 235 - 573$ is about 4150

Exercise 2.2A _____

1 Give an estimate for each of these.

   a 48×61 **b** 72×97 **c** 33×57 **d** 56×61
   e 72×87 **f** 92×49 **g** 29×34 **h** 78×104

2 A river ferry can carry 78 passengers. In a week the ferry
   makes 207 crossings. Estimate the greatest total number
   of passengers carried in the week.

3 A hockey club buys 72 sets of their new strip for £3465.
   Estimate the cost of each set of new strip.

Exercise 2.2B _____

1 Estimate each of these. Show your working.

   a 47×122 **b** 66×185 **c** 294×53 **d** 493×27
   e $563 \div 48$ **f** $797 \div 18$ **g** $1392 \div 47$ **h** 218×194

2 This data gives the number of miles travelled by a lorry in
   five days.

   Day 1: 1437, Day 2: 1022, Day 3: 717,
   Day 4: 971, Day 5: 1231

   Estimate the total distance travelled for the five days.

3 In seven days 128 346 people visited a theme park.
   This was estimated as 12 850 people each day.
   Explain how you think this estimate was worked out.

2.3 Adding integers on paper

You can add numbers on paper.
You must line up the place values first.

> An integer is any whole
> number.

Example

Show your working for this calculation. $7563 + 878$

Write the numbers one above the other to
match the place values and add each column.

> Remember to show the
> carry numbers.

$$
\begin{array}{r}
7563 \\
+878 \\
\hline
8441 \\
\text{\small 1 1 1}
\end{array}
$$

$3 + 8 = 11$
$60 + 70 + 10 = 140$
$500 + 800 + 100 = 1400$
$7000 + 1000 = 8000$

Exercise 2.3A

Show your working for each of these questions.

1 Find:
   a $735 + 879$ **b** $865 + 978$ **c** $504 + 688$ **d** $295 + 486$
   e $8456 + 287$ **f** $655 + 7846$ **g** $786 + 8876$ **h** $867 + 5879$

2 Find:
   a $3088 + 17 + 375$ **b** $45 + 3627 + 564$ **c** $5089 + 15 + 657$ **d** $8706 + 734 + 19$

3 The passenger numbers for a tram service were:
   Monday 3655, Tuesday 1088, Wednesday 178
   a Which day did most people use the tram?
   b Find the total number of people for the three days.

4 This data gives the number of T-shirts printed on each of
   five days.
   Day 1: 688, Day 2: 727, Day 3: 835,
   Day 4: 913, Day 5: 457
   a How many T-shirts in total were printed in the first
      three days?
   b How many in total were printed in the last three days?
   c Find the total printed for the five days.

Exercise 2.3B

Show your working for each calculation.

1 Find:
   a $454 + 874 + 78$ **b** $994 + 47 + 283$ **c** $4052 + 88 + 34 + 675$
   d $78 + 5723 + 81675$ **e** $485 + 67 + 9756$ **f** $588 + 47 + 7439$

2 Three trains took fans to a match.
   Train 1 took 15 643 fans, Train 2 took 14 884 fans and
   Train 3 took 12 856 fans.
   In total how many fans went on these trains?

3 This data gives the number of cans of cola made on each
   of five days.
   Day 1; 27 655, Day 2: 24 870, Day 3: 26 085,
   Day 4: 25 735, Day 5: 26 775
   a How many cans were made in total over the first three days?
   b How many cans in total were made in the last three days?
   c In total, how many cans were made in the five days?

2.4 Subtracting integers on paper

You can subtract numbers on paper.
You must line up the place values first.

Example

Show your working for this calculation. $5104 - 357$

Line up the units.
Subtract the units first.

$$
\begin{array}{r}
{}^{4}\cancel{5}\,{}^{10}\cancel{1}\,{}^{9}\cancel{0}\,{}^{1}\cancel{4} \\
-\quad 3\;5\;7 \\
\hline
4\;7\;4\;7
\end{array}
$$

'take' a ten from the tens column

$14 - 7 = 7$
$90 - 50 = 40$
$1000 - 300 = 700$
$4000 - 0 = 4000$

> Take the bottom number from the top number in each column.
> Make sure there is enough to take away from in each column before you start.

Exercise 2.4A

1 Show your working for each of these calculations.

a $4308 - 259$	**b** $4035 - 578$	**c** $6107 - 329$	**d** $3002 - 575$
e $2524 - 565$	**f** $34\,045 - 7607$	**g** $21\,040 - 5864$	**h** $13\,002 - 8347$

2 A firm has 24 085 customers, 14 368 of them are female.
   How many customers are male?

3 In two days a sorting office sorted 1 500 000 letters.
   The first day 1 027 574 letters were sorted.
   How many were sorted on the second day?

4 In 1997 an airline had 6 124 188 passengers, in 1998 the
   figure was 7 065 135.
   How many more passengers were carried in 1998?

Exercise 2.4B

1 Show your calculation for each of these:

a $6054 - 785$	**b** $3080 - 277$	**c** $7021 - 952$	**d** $6005 - 726$
e $22\,105 - 8437$	**f** $80\,021 - 3257$	**g** $7002 - 4254$	**h** $30\,103 - 7857$

2 A supporters club has one hundred and fifty five thousand
   members. Of these 65 371 live in the UK.
   How many do not live in the UK?

3 Copy and complete this table. Show your working.

Letter delivery

Round	First Class	Second Class	Total
A	623	☐	1305
B	☐	1032	2657
C	☐	12 134	15 023
D	15 788	☐	22 114

This type of table is known as a two-way table.

4 A building cost £3 million to build. Costs are materials and labour. The materials cost £14 237. Work out the labour costs. Show your working.

2.5 Multiplying integers on paper

You can multiply numbers on paper like this:

Most people know this as long multiplication.

Example

Show your working for this calculation. 376×53

$$
\begin{array}{r}
3\,7\,3 \\
\times \quad\quad 5\,3 \\
\hline
1_{3}8_{1}6\,5\,0 \\
1_{2}1\,1\,9 \\
\hline
1\,9\,7\,6\,9
\end{array}
$$

Start multiplying by the 50
Now multiply by the 3
Now add

The digit 5 stands for 50. Any number multiplied by 50 will end with zero. Put zero in the units column before you multiply by the digit 5.

In this method you work out 50×373 and 3×373, then add the two results.

Exercise 2.5A _____

1 Show how you calculate each of these:

   a 37×45 **b** 82×37 **c** 63×58 **d** 36×87
   e 65×39 **f** 68×75 **g** 94×52 **h** 74×88

2 Show how you calculate each of these:

   a 254×36 **b** 374×82 **c** 546×73 **d** 684×81
   e 724×58 **f** 845×57 **g** 763×64 **h** 488×49

Exercise 2.5B

1 Copy and complete this multiplication table.
   Show all your working.

×	386	575	94	479	683	86	304
74							
65							19 760

This is 304 × 65

2 This data is for two buses.

Bus 37B   : Route length 72 km   number of journeys 653
Bus 518Ex : Route length 374 km   number of journeys 78

   a In total, how far did Bus 37B travel?
   b In total, how far did Bus 518Ex travel?
   c Which bus travelled further and by how much?

2.6 Dividing integers on paper

You can divide large numbers using this method:

Example 1

Show your working for this calculation. $4376 \div 8$

$$8 \overline{)4^4 3^3 7^5 6} \quad \text{so} \quad 4376 \div 8 = 547$$
$$0\ 5\ 4\ 7$$

8 into 4 is 0 rem 4
8 into 43 is 5 rem 3
8 into 37 is 4 rem 5
8 into 56 is 7 rem 0

Example 2

Show how you work out: $966 \div 14$

$$14 \overline{)9^9 6^{12} 6} \quad \text{so} \quad 966 \div 14 = 69$$
$$0\ 6\ 9$$

14 into 9 is 0 rem 9
14 into 96 is 6 rem 12
14 into 126 is 9 rem 0

Exercise 2.6A _____

1 Show how you work out each of these:

    a $4599 \div 7$ **b** $3140 \div 4$ **c** $3498 \div 6$ **d** $2601 \div 3$

    e $6072 \div 8$ **f** $7875 \div 9$ **g** $4485 \div 5$ **h** $5243 \div 7$

2 Show how you work out:

    a $3366 \div 6$ **b** $4123 \div 7$ **c** $3948 \div 4$ **d** $6832 \div 8$

    e $3705 \div 5$ **f** $7668 \div 9$ **g** $8778 \div 7$ **h** $8472 \div 6$

3 A firm buys 15 identical tents and a box with 975 tent pegs. How many pegs are needed for each tent?

Exercise 2.6B _____

1 Show how you calculate each of these:

    a $780 \div 12$ **b** $960 \div 15$ **c** $972 \div 18$ **d** $923 \div 13$

    e $928 \div 16$ **f** $357 \div 17$ **g** $705 \div 15$ **h** $768 \div 16$

2 A drilling platform with 16 legs weighs a total of 960 tonnes. Each leg takes an equal share of the weight. Work out the weight taken by each leg.

3 An aircraft costs £22 million. Lazyjet orders some of these aircraft at a total cost of 990 million. How many aircraft do Lazyjet order?

2.7 Money and the calculator

You can use a calculator for money calculations.

▶ You need to be able to interpret a calculator display properly.

Example 1

Calculate: £127.56 + £378.21 + £1256 + 83 p

You key in   127.56 + 378.21 + 1256 + 0.83

                The calculator display will show: `1762.6`   This display shows: 60 p **not** 6 p.

                This means: £1762.60

You need to remember whether you are working in pence or £s.

Example 2

A market trader bought 6753 notepads for £202.05
Find the price paid for each notepad.

You need to calculate £202.05 ÷ 6735
The display will show: 0.03
This means: 3 pence

> The calculation is in £s.
> The display shows £0.03

Exercise 2.7A _____

1 List the key presses for each of these calculations.

   a £12.48 + £4.65 + 86 p   **b** 45 p + £12.73 + 6 p + £5   **c** 57 p + £34.55 + 8 p

2 These are the results of calculations in £s. What sum of
   money is displayed in each?

   a 2.4   **b** 8.1   **c** 0.7   **d** 0.03
   e 0.9   **f** 5.2   **g** 0.01   **h** 1.1

3 Write a calculation that gives this display as a result: 0.08

Exercise 2.7B _____

1 How does a calculator display each of these amounts in pounds (£s)?

   a 24 p   **b** two pounds and six pence   **c** five pounds forty pence
   d 7 p   **e** six pounds ten pence   **f** six pounds and a penny

2 Complete these calculations for a calculator display
   showing £5.08 as the answer.

   a £3.29 + ☐ =   **b** ☐ × 4 =   **c** £81.28 ÷ ☐ =   **d** £26.65 − ☐ =

3 Working in £s, a display shows 0.038.
   What does this mean as an amount of money?

_____

A calculator calculates, it does not work out correct
answers.

For correct answers you must:

- key in the data and instructions accurately
- interpret the display for the answer
- check the answer using an estimate.

> This is true for any
> calculation you do with a
> calculator.

Example 3

This calculation is keyed in:

£3.44 + £127.56 + £19.99 + 39 p =

The display shows the answer   £189.99

Use an estimate to show the answer is incorrect.

Estimate the answer: £3 + £128 + £20 = £151

So the answer in the display must be wrong. It is too large!

> Try the calculation
> yourself.
> 39 p was keyed in as 39,
> To key in 39 p here you
> must key in 0.39

Exercise 2.7C

1 For this calculation:

£57.99 + £26.37 + £2.95 + 55 p + £1.06

a Estimate the answer. Explain how you calculated your estimate.

b With a calculator find the accurate answer.

2 Jim uses a calculator for this:

67 p + 88 p + £1.24 + 57 p + £2.76

He gives an answer of £2.16

a What is your estimate of the answer?

b What is the correct answer?

c Explain the mistakes you think Jim made.

3 Estimate 2500 × £1.69 and explain how you calculated your estimate.

Exercise 2.7D

1 a Estimate the answer for this calculation:

£157.99 + £312.49 + £18.55 + £2.75

Jes estimated the answer as £370.

b Do you think this is a good estimate? Explain.

c Explain how you think Jes calculated her estimate.

d Find the exact answer.

2 In a money calculation the display shows 0.15

a What is the most this can mean?

b What is the least the display can mean?

3 Jan buys 24 000 badges for £3960.
   She estimates the cost of one badge as 20 p.
   a Do you think this is a good estimate? Explain.
   b Calculate the actual cost of one badge.
   She sells the badges at 25 p each.
   c Calculate the total profit she will make if
        she sells every badge.

> Profit = Total received − total cost

2.8 Using brackets and the order of operations

You can use brackets to package a calculation so that it can
only give one answer. Without brackets it is often possible
to find more than one answer.

Example 1

Calculate the value of: $4 + 5 \times 3 - 1$

Think of it this way: $4 + 5 \times 3 - 1 = 9 \times 3 - 1 = 27 - 1 = 26$
Brackets for this answer $(4 + 5) \times 3 - 1 = 26$

Or, think of it this way: $4 + 5 \times 3 - 1 = 4 + 15 - 1 = 19 - 1 = 18$
Brackets for this answer $4 + (5 \times 3) - 1 = 18$

Or, think of it this way: $4 + 5 \times 3 - 1 = 4 + 10 = 14$
Brackets for this answer $4 + 5 \times (3 - 1) = 14$

> Work out the
> calculation in
> the bracket
> first.

Exercise 2.8A

1 Copy each calculation and put brackets in to give the
   answer shown.
   a $5 + 9 \times 4 = 41$ **b** $5 + 9 \times 4 = 56$
   c $6 + 9 \times 4 = 60$ **d** $6 + 9 \times 4 = 42$
   e $25 + 5 \times 4 = 120$ **f** $24 \div 8 + 5 = 8$
   g $5 \times 5 - 3 = 10$ **h** $15 \times 5 - 3 = 72$

2 Copy and complete each calculation.
   a $(12 + 4) \times 3 - 18 =$ **b** $35 \div (7 - 2) =$
   c $(35 \div 7) - 2 =$ **d** $23 - (5 \times 4) =$
   e $(19 + 5 - 22) \times 16 =$ **f** $(42 \div 7) + 19 =$
   g $(66 \div 11) - (48 \div 24) =$ **h** $12 \times (15 - 7) \div 2 =$

Exercise 2.8B _____

1 Copy each calculation and put brackets in to give the
answer shown.

   a $13 - 5 \times 7 + 2 = 72$ **b** $13 + 5 \times 7 + 2 = 50$
   c $12 \times 4 + 5 - 25 = 28$ **d** $63 \div 9 - 12 + 15 = 10$

2 Copy and complete each calculation.

   a $15 + (54 \div 3) - 32 =$ **b** $(16 - 5) \times (5 + 7) =$
   c $(44 - 8) \div (26 - 17) =$ **d** $4 \times (5 - 17 + 22) \div 8 =$

3 Copy and complete each of these.

   a $(12 + 4) \div (6 - 2) \times 5 =$ **b** $(5 - 2) \times (16 + 1) - 50 =$
   c $(34 - 9) \div (22 - 17) =$ **d** $(56 \div 7) \times (13 - 8) + 1 =$
   e $(2 + 3 - 4) \times (16 - 7) \div 3 =$ **f** $(16 - 7) \times (1 + 2 + 3) - 22 =$
   g $(23 + 5 - 19) \div (15 - 12) \times 2 =$ **h** $(35 - 28) \times (3 + 5) \div (15 + 13) =$

_____

If a calculation has brackets you work out the value of the
bracket first.
For the rest of the calculation you do each mathematical
operation in order.
This rule will help you remember the order:

The rule is BoDMAS

It stands for: **B**rackets first then
                Division then
                Multiplication then
                Addition then
                Subtraction.

The four operations are:
add, subtract, **multiply**
and **divide**.

Example 2

Use BoDMAS to evaluate these:

   a $(3 + 5) \times 4 - 9 = 8 \times 4 - 9 = 32 - 9 = 23$

   b $(9 - 3) \times (15 - 8) = 6 \times 7 = 42$

   c $3 + 14 \times (7 - 4) = 3 + 14 \times 3 = 3 + 42 = 45$

   d $5 + 3 \times 5 - 24 \div 8 = 5 + 3 \times 5 - 3 = 5 + 15 - 3 = 17$

Most calculators work to
BoDMAS rules.
Use these examples to
check that yours does.

Exercise 2.8C

1 Use BoDMAS to work out:

a $16 + 5 \times 4 - 42 \div 7 =$ b $72 \div 9 - 15 + 7 \times 3 =$
c $54 \div 6 - 15 + 3 \times (17 - 12) =$ d $45 \div 9 + (13 - 5) \times 3 - 32 =$
e $12 \times (25 - 13) \div 48 + 15 =$ f $120 \div (15 - 7) + 9 \times 3 - 35 =$

2 Copy and complete each of these using BoDMAS.

a $(6 + 3) \times 5 - 36 \div 9 =$ b $(135 - 15) \div (3 + 4 + 5) =$
c $13 - 5 + 28 \div 4 \times 5 + 1 =$ d $135 \div 3 \times (21 - 17) =$

3 Write a calculation that uses BoDMAS and gives an answer of 10.

Exercise 2.8D

1 Use BoDMAS to work out:

a $56 \div 8 + 3 \times (35 - 28) =$ b $3 \times 5 + 108 \div (12 - 9) =$
c $(19 + 24) + 5 - 96 \div 4 =$ d $(35 + 19) \div (13 + 14) \times 55 =$
e $(19 + 36) \div (8 - 3) \div (8 - 5) =$ f $(16 \times 5 + 170) \div 50 - 4 - 1 =$

2 Use BoDMAS to work out:

a $(12 + 8) \times 2 - 20 \div (7 + 3) =$ b $60 \div 5 + 13 \times 3 - (7.5 \times 2) =$
c $95 - 54 \div 9 + 2 \times (4 + 2) - 1 =$ d $99 \div 11 - 6 \times 4 + 2 \times 9 =$

3 Write a calculation that uses BoDMAS, with brackets, that gives an answer of 8.

2.9 To find a simple fraction of an amount

▶ To find $\frac{1}{2}$ of an amount you divide the amount by 2.

Example 1

Find $\frac{1}{2}$ of £340

$$\frac{1}{2} \text{ of } £340 = 340 \div 2$$
$$= 170$$

So $\frac{1}{2}$ of £340 is £170

▶ To find $\frac{1}{5}$ of an amount you divide the amount by 5.

Example 2

Find $\frac{1}{5}$ of £210

$$\frac{1}{5} \text{ of } £210 = 210 \div 5$$
$$= 42$$

So $\frac{1}{5}$ of £210 is £42

Exercise 2.9A

1 Find $\frac{1}{2}$ of:

  a £560   **b** £780   **c** £1050   **d** £6080

2 Find $\frac{1}{8}$ of:

  a £88   **b** £24   **c** 800 cm   **d** £728

3 Find $\frac{1}{5}$ of:

  a £15   **b** 450 kg   **c** £1050   **d** £3000

4 Find $\frac{1}{6}$ of:

  a £54   **b** £78   **c** 102 metres **d** £240

Exercise 2.9B

1 Find $\frac{1}{3}$ of:

  a £42   **b** 57 m   **c** £120   **d** £156

2 Find $\frac{1}{7}$ of:

  a £56   **b** £84   **c** 147 cm   **d** £350

3 Find $\frac{1}{4}$ of:

  a £96   **b** 136 kg   **c** 580 km   **d** £920

4 Find $\frac{1}{9}$ of:

  a £81   **b** 108 km   **c** 270 cm   **d** £999

2.10 To find any fraction of an amount

▶ To find a fraction of an amount you:

- multiply the amount by the top number of the fraction, then
- divide the answer by the bottom number of the fraction.

> The top number of a fraction is the **numerator**, the bottom number is the **denominator**.

Example

Find $\frac{3}{4}$ of £72

Multiply £72 by 3 then divide the answer by 4.

$$72 \times 3 = 216$$
$$216 \div 4 = 54$$

So $\frac{3}{4}$ of £72 = £54

Exercise 2.10A _____

1 Calculate $\frac{3}{4}$ of £60.

2 Calculate $\frac{3}{5}$ of £80.

3 Calculate:

   a $\frac{1}{6}$ of 48   **b** $\frac{3}{6}$ of 48   **c** $\frac{5}{6}$ of 48   **d** $\frac{3}{8}$ of 48

4 Calculate:

   a $\frac{5}{7}$ of 140   **b** $\frac{2}{5}$ of 80   **c** $\frac{4}{9}$ of 72   **d** $\frac{2}{3}$ of 63

   e $\frac{2}{3}$ of 99   **f** $\frac{5}{12}$ of 72   **g** $\frac{6}{11}$ of 55   **h** $\frac{4}{5}$ of 70

Exercise 2.10B _____

1 Find:

   a $\frac{3}{5}$ of 20   **b** $\frac{5}{8}$ of 72   **c** $\frac{9}{10}$ of 150   **d** $\frac{3}{4}$ of 56

   e $\frac{5}{8}$ of 48   **f** $\frac{6}{7}$ of 56   **g** $\frac{3}{4}$ of 40   **h** $\frac{7}{9}$ of 45

2 In a group of 160 students, $\frac{5}{8}$ were female.
   How many students were male?

3 Calculate $\frac{3}{4}$ of £760.

4 There are 1740 elm trees in a park.
   About $\frac{5}{6}$ of the elm trees in the park are dead.
   How many elm trees in the park are dead?

5 Andy said Alex spent $\frac{3}{4}$ of last week in bed. How many hours is this?

6 Find $\frac{3}{8}$ of £424.

Remember:
24 hours in day.
7 days in a week.

2.11 Simple percentages of an amount

▶ You need to know some simple fractions as percentages:

$\frac{1}{2} = 50\%$ $\frac{1}{4} = 25\%$ $\frac{1}{10} = 10\%$ $\frac{1}{5} = 20\%$

▶ You can find other percentages like this:

Example 1

Find 15% of £460

15% is the same as 10% + 5% (half of 10%)

10% of £460 $= \frac{1}{10} \times$ £460 $=$ £46

5% of £460 $= \frac{1}{2} \times$ £46 $=$ £23

so 15% of £460 $=$ £46 + £23 $=$ £69

Example 2

Find 35% of 280

35% is the same as 25% + 10%

25% of 280 $= \frac{1}{4} \times 280 = 70$

10% of 280 $= \frac{1}{10} \times 280 = 28$

so 35% of 280 $= 70 + 28 = 98$

Exercise 2.11A

1 From the fractions and percentages above how could you find:

   a 20%   **b** 60%   **c** 40%

   d 85%   **e** 65%   **f** 30%?

You should not need a calculator to do problems like these. Just remember the easy percentages.

2 Calculate each of these, show all your working.

   a 20% of £50   **b** 60% of 600 people

   c 40% of 820 boxes   **d** 80% of £45

   e 75% of 80 tins   **f** 90% of 300 cats

3 Vicky must pay 40% of £12 000.
How much must she pay?

4 Carlo says 15% of the cars he sells are red.
He sold 400 cars last year. How many were red?

Exercise 2.11B

1 Find each of these, show all your working.
    a 35% of £700   **b** 5% of £60   **c** 45% of $360
    d 15% of 80 stamps   **e** 65% of £500   **f** 95% of 200 birds

2 a Find 25% of £240   **b** Now work out 12.5% of £240

3 Explain how you could work out $7\frac{1}{2}\%$ of something.

2.12 Finding any percentage of an amount

To find a percentage of an amount, follow the method in the
example:

Example

Find 34% of £350

$$34\% \times £350 = 34 \div 100 \times £350$$
$$= £119 \text{ (with a calculator)}$$

So 34% of £350 is £119

Exercise 2.12A

1 a What is 52% as a decimal?
    b Find 52% of £650.

2 Copy and complete:
    a 45% = 0.45   so   45% of £600 is £☐
    b 24% = ☐   so   24% of £150 is £☐
    c 6% = ☐   so   6% of £850 is £☐
    d 65% = ☐   so   65% of 360 kg is ☐ kg

Remember:
5% is 0.05

3 a What is 36% as a decimal?
   b Work out 36% of £1500.

4 At a match 36 000 cans of cola were sold.
   34% of these were diet cola.
   How many cans of diet cola were sold?

Exercise 2.12B _____

1 Write 7% as a decimal.

2 Calculate:
   a 44% of £50   **b** 8% of 300 miles   **c** 83% of £250
   d 55% of 360 kg   **e** 12% of 850 metres   **f** 4% of 2500 km

3 Calculate:
   a 7% of £4600   **b** 2% of 400 000 Euros   **c** 9% of 450 kg   **d** 3% of 35 000 km

4 Calculate each answer in pounds and pence.
   a 35% of £630   **b** 58% of £56
   c 78% of £625   **d** 17% of £124
   e 32% of £361   **f** 57% of £93
   g 8% of £331   **h** 3% of £1627

> Think about how money is displayed by a calculator.

2.13 Percentage problems

Exercise 2.13A _____

1 1600 fans went to a match.
   34% of these fans went by train.
   a How many fans went by train?
   b What percentage of fans did not go by train?

2 A shop sold 360 bikes in June.
   10% were classic bikes, 25% were childrens' bikes,
   40% were ATBs and 5% were secondhand.
   Copy and complete this table.

Type of bike	Percentage sold	Number sold in June
Classic	10%	
Childrens'		
ATBs		
Secondhand		

3 1280 people live in the village of Stockdon.
35% of them own a car.

   a How many people own a car?
   b How many do not own a car?

4 There are 21 000 seats in a stadium.
45% are for season ticket holders.

   a How many seats are for season ticket holders?
   b What percentage of the seats are not for season ticket holders?

Exercise 2.13B

1 In a car park there are 4700 cars.
21% are red, 17% are blue, 33% are diesels,
2% are left-hand drive, 52% have 4 doors.
Copy and complete this table for the cars in the car park.

Type	Number of cars
Red	
Blue	
Diesel	
Left-hand drive	
4-door	

2 Last year 3 600 000 cars crossed a bridge.
31% of these cars carried only the driver.
How many cars was this?

3 On one day 6600 students were late for school.
This table shows the reasons given.

Reason	Percentage	Number
Overslept	16%	
Bus was late	28%	
Forgot something	11%	
Finishing homework	24%	
Other reasons	☐%	

   a What percentage had other reasons?
   b Copy and complete the table.

4 6% of the accidents in Bantron involve cyclists.
There were 17 000 accidents in Bantron last year.
  a What percentage of accidents do not involve cyclists?
  b Last year how many accidents involved cyclists?

2.14 Working with ratios

Ratio is a way of comparing different parts of a whole.
You can divide a quantity into unequal parts using ratio.

Example 1

Divide £28 in the ratio 3:4.

  The ratio is   3 parts : 4 parts
  which is a total of $3 + 4 = 7$ parts

So the £28 must be divided into 7 equal parts, which are
then put in the ratio 3:4.

To find 1 part   £28 ÷ 7 = £4

For 3 parts $3 \times £4 = £12$
For 4 parts $4 \times £4 = £16$

So, £28 divided in the ratio 3:4 is   £12 : £16

Check: £12 + £16 = £28

> You should check your
> answer each time.

Example 2

Divide 2130 km in the ratio 2:5:8.

  The ratio is   2 parts : 5 parts : 8 parts
  which is a total of $2 + 5 + 8 = 15$ parts

To find 1 part   2130 ÷ 15 = 142

For 2 parts $2 \times 142 = 284$
For 5 parts $5 \times 142 = 710$
For 8 parts $8 \times 142 = 1136$

So, 2130 km divided in the ratio 2:5:8 is,   284 km : 710 km : 1136 km

Check: 284 km + 710 km + 1136 km = 2130 km

Exercise 2.14A

1 Divide:

    a £56   in the ratio $3:5$
    b £63   in the ratio $4:5$
    c £108   in the ratio $5:7$
    d £416   in the ratio $9:7$
    e £943   in the ratio $15:8$

> **Remember:**
> Check your answers.

2 Divide:

    a 5005 km   in the ratio $4:5:2$
    b 930 km   in the ratio $7:3:5$
    c 1740 km   in the ratio $5:3:7$
    d 6516 km   in the ratio $9:4:5$
    e 16 000 km in the ratio $9:4:7$

> Check each answer, even if you use a calculator.

3 A recipe for a sauce to serve four people uses:

    200 g of butter, 320 g of flour, 200 ml of stock

How much of each item is needed if you change the recipe to serve six people?

> Ratio is often asked about in word problems like this.

Exercise 2.14B

1 Divide £705.28 in the ratio $9:8$.

2 Divide 2088 km in the ratio $8:13:3$.

3 A sponsored walk makes a total £3368.61 for charity.
The money is given to the charities:
Treescape, Shelter at Night, Infant Line and
Animal Rescue in the ratio $2:9:6:4$
How much is given to each charity?

> To answer a word problem:
> - read the question
> - decide on the data
> - do the working out
> - write an answer.

4 Dave, Liam and Mary share a lottery win of £30 645.
They share the win in the ratio $2:3:4$.
How much does each of them win?

5 A dye is made from red, blue, yellow, and black.
The colours are used in the ratio $2:5:9:4$.
A mix of 1000 litres of dye is made.
How much of each colour is used?

You can also think of ratios in this way.

Example 3

Three cyclists take part in a race.
Jan, Kim and Ryan do the distance in the ratio 7 : 3 : 4.
Kim cycles 177 km, how far do Jan and Ryan cycle?

The ratio gives   Jan : Kim : Ryan
                    7 :   3   :   4
                    ☐ : 177 km : ☐

> Show the data like this
> and you will find it easier
> to work things out.

So, Kim does 3 parts which is 177 km

3 parts is 177 km, so   1 part = $177 \div 3 = 59$ km

Jan does 7 parts which is $7 \times 59 = 413$ km
Kim does 3 parts which is   177 km
Ryan does 4 parts which is $4 \times 59 = 236$ km

So, Jan does 413 km and Ryan does 236 km.

Exercise 2.14C

1 Three cyclists take part in a race.
  Ian, Karen and Connor complete distances in the ratio 4 : 5 : 7.
  Connor cycles 350 km. How far do Ian and Karen cycle?

2 The players in a hockey club are in the ratio 3 : 7 male to
  female. The club has 48 male players.
  How many of the players are female?

3 The length and width of a rectangle are in the ratio 9 : 4.
  The length of the rectangle is 45 cm.
  Work out the width of the rectangle.

4 Sunfresh is a mix of water and fruit juice in the ratio
  9 : 15. A mix uses 1050 litres of juice.
  How much water is in the mix?

Exercise 2.14D

1 The sales of Cara, Wilja and Desiree potatoes are in the ratio
  15 : 9 : 11. We know that 1947 tonnes of Desiree were sold.
  a How many tonnes of Cara were sold?
  b How many tonnes of Wilja were sold?

2 Sales of skimmed, semi-skimmed and whole milk are in
  the ratio 3 : 9 : 4. Sales of whole milk were 544 litres.
  How much of the other types were sold?

3 Traffic over a bridge was found to be
cars : vans : lorries in the ratio 12 : 5 : 3.
In a week 1050 vans crossed the bridge.
How many cars and lorries crossed the bridge?

4 A bakery uses white, brown and rye flour in the ratio
12 : 9 : 4. In a month the bakery uses 432 kg of rye flour.
How much of the other types of flour are used?

5 A recipe for 12 biscuits uses:

      300 g of butter, 600 g of flour and 200 g of sugar

How much of each ingredient is needed to make 15 biscuits?

2.15 Rounding to the nearest integer

You can round a decimal value to a whole number to help
you estimate the value of a calculation. You need to
consider the value of the first digit after the decimal point.

> **Remember:**
> An integer is a whole number.

▶ If the first digit after the decimal point is: 0, 1, 2, 3 or 4
                            the number is rounded down.
  If the first digit after the decimal point is: 5, 6, 7, 8 or 9
                            the number is rounded up.

Example 1

Round 12.65 to the nearest integer.

The first digit after the decimal place is 6 so

      12.65 will be rounded up to 13

> On a number line 12.65 is closer to 13 than it is to 12.

Example 2

Estimate the answer to 8.72×3.45

- Round the decimal numbers
     8.72   round to 9
     3.45   rounds to 3
- Estimate the answer
     $9 \times 3 = 27$

So, the answer to 8.72×3.45 is about 27

Exercise 2.15A

1 Round each of these decimal values to the nearest integer.

a 12.35	**b** 16.72	**c** 5.08
d 34.42	**e** 46.56	**f** 58.29
g 30.08	**h** 156.67	**i** 124.51

2 Round each of these decimal values to the nearest integer.

a 1.76	**b** 1.125	**c** 5.08
d 1.09	**e** 1.499	**f** 0.85

3 In each of these calculations:

- round the values to the nearest integer
- estimate the answer.

a 4.62×5.3	**b** 7.5×4.66
c 1.08×9.4	**d** 9.3×9.72
e 4.8×3.099	**f** 6.48×8.07
g 19.74×3.38	**h** 12.29×6.56

4 Estimate the answer to each of these by first rounding to the nearest whole number.

a 34.6×1.88	**b** $16.25 \div 7.62$
c $24.075 \div 2.75$	**d** $3.56 \times 5.35 \times 7.83$
e $8.85 \times 3.72 \div 5.62$	**f** $44.74 \div 8.81$
g $12.39 \times 2.62 \div 8.75$	**h** $99.66 \div 20.395$

Exercise 2.15B

1 Round each of these decimal values to the nearest integer.

a 54.68	**b** 35.099	**c** 26.52	**d** 106.21
e 39.75	**f** 40.19	**g** 99.82	**h** 119.385
i 30.61	**j** 121.08	**k** 0.683	**l** 1.099

2 Estimate the answer to each of these by first rounding to the nearest whole number.

a 24.6×7.2	**b** 38.4×4.5
c 124.7×3.49	**d** 35.3×21.6
e 1.075×235.48	**f** $23.82 \div 5.75$
g $56.48 \div 6.83$	**h** $63.29 \div 8.88$
i $12.4 \times 4.75 \div 19.6$	**j** $25.48 \times 3.82 \div 10.4$

3 Estimate the answer to each of these by first rounding to
the nearest whole number.

a	$15.4 \div 2.75$	**b**	$29.62 \div 5.35$
c	$49.28 \div 6.57$	**d**	$41.88 \div 5.75$
e	$72.085 \div 9.385$	**f**	$71.58 \div 8.84$
g	$119.55 \div 12.425$	**h**	$51.25 \div 16.71$

2.16 Adding and subtracting decimals

You can add or subtract decimals by keeping place values
matched.
Very often you can do the calculation mentally.
Before you calculate an exact answer you should estimate
the answer.

> Round to the nearest integer for your estimate.

▶ You can do a decimal calculation mentally by adding the two parts of the number
separately.

Example 1: mental method

Calculate the value of: $14.8 + 7.6 + 8.2$

Estimate the answer: $14 + 8 + 8 = 30$

To work out the answer mentally:
- add the decimal part $.8 + .6 + .2 = 1.6$
- add the whole number part $14 + 7 + 8 = 29$
- add the two parts $29 + 1.6 = 30.6$

So, $14.8 + 7.6 + 8.2 = 30.6$

Example 2: written method

Calculate the value of: $16.44 + 3.8 + 1.08$

Estimate the answer: $16 + 4 + 1 = 21$

To calculate the answer:
- write the numbers under each other   16.44
  to match the place values   3.8
                                             1.08
- add the columns   21.32
                                             ‾‾‾‾‾
                                             1 1 1

> Line up the decimal points and the place values match.

Exercise 2.16A _____

1 Use a mental method to calculate:

a 4.8 + 5.6	**b** 3.7 + 6.5
c 5.4 + 6.3	**d** 8.2 + 1.07
e 3.8 + 4.2	**f** 12.6 + 11.8
g 6.4 + 5.18	**h** 15.2 + 2.84
i 23.4 + 8.58	**j** 4.2 + 14.68

Remember to estimate each answer first.

2 Use a written method to find:

a 28.65 + 35.68	**b** 46.07 + 64 + 85
c 15.75 + 23.84	**d** 8.46 + 15.8 + 22.34
e 5.85 + 4.6 + 9.26	**f** 11.68 + 9.6 + 15.48
g 4.56 + 8.7 + 12.05	**h** 13.72 + 6.5 + 8.92
i 27.4 + 16.69 + 3.07	**j** 22.27 + 13.4 + 2.72

Exercise 2.16B _____

1 Use a written method to work out:

a 15.8 + 7.65 + 8.35	**b** 9.05 + 12.43 + 4.76
c 22.6 + 17.54 + 22.8	**d** 26.5 + 14.43 + 18.28
e 45.8 + 22.53 + 17.81	**f** 44.75 + 3.08 + 0.84
g 56.7 + 34.58 + 12.75	**h** 36.48 + 18.04 + 65.8
i 3.04 + 0.85 + 16.4	**j** 0.4 + 0.06 + 0.55

2 Use a mental method to work out:

a 3.6 + 5.4	**b** 1.25 + 14.6
c 9.2 + 4.05	**d** 3.4 + 5.2 + 9.8
e 7.7 + 6.05 + 11.2	**f** 4.5 + 18.2 + 8.4
g 5.72 + 3.6	**h** 3.22 + 15.95
i 45.3 + 56.62	**j** 15.4 + 6.85

You can subtract decimal numbers by matching place values.
You match place values by matching the decimal points.

▶ You can do the calculation mentally by counting on.

Example 3: mental method

Calculate the value of: 66.2 − 53.8

Estimate the answer: 66 − 54 = 12

To calculate the answer mentally:

- count on from 53.8 to 54   this gives   0.2
- count on from 54 to 66   this gives   12.2
- count on from 66 to 66.2   this gives   12.4

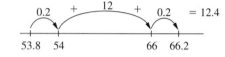

So, 66.2 − 53.8 = 12.4

The answer is close to the estimate and so is probably right.

Example 4: written method

Calculate the value of: 78.62 − 24.76

Estimate the answer: 80 − 25 = 55

To calculate the answer:

- write the numbers under each other
  to match the place values
- subtract the columns

$$\begin{array}{r} 78.62 \\ 24.76 \\ \hline 53.86 \end{array}$$

So, 78.62 − 24.76 = 53.86

Exercise 2.16C

1 Use a mental method to work out:

   a 12.4 − 8.5   **b** 7.5 − 3.8

   c 24.6 − 13.7   **d** 18.4 − 7.7

   e 34.2 − 17.5   **f** 19.2 − 15.8

   g 38.7 − 17.4   **h** 20.6 − 13.5

   i 25.2 − 18.8   **j** 30.6 − 16.5

> Try counting on, you might find it easier.

2 Use a written method to work out each of these.
You must show your working.

   a 145.6 − 57.88   **b** 560.4 − 165.57

   c 675.3 − 496.58   **d** 45.06 − 29.7

   e 2.07 − 0.85   **f** 0.8 − 0.09

   g 0.7 − 0.07   **h** 157.08 − 0.7

   i 6.5 − 5.56   **j** 14.85 − 9.76

Exercise 2.16D _____

1 Use a mental method to work out:

    a $34.6 - 25.7$ **b** $67.8 - 45.4$
    c $58.7 - 38.8$ **d** $85.3 - 57.5$
    e $166.8 - 165.5$ **f** $204.1 - 67.5$
    g $565.4 - 456.8$ **h** $404.4 - 294.4$
    i $60.07 - 57.1$ **j** $800.1 - 408.8$

2 Use a written method to work out each of these.
    You must show your working.

> Remember to estimate each answer.

    a $20.05 - 16.78$ **b** $45.3 - 37.28$
    c $40.08 - 37.72$ **d** $55.55 - 38.88$
    e $206.06 - 87.59$ **f** $104.04 - 44.44$
    g $675.32 - 275.84$ **h** $709.25 - 576.78$
    i $3.08 - 0.19$ **j** $7.4 - 0.75$

2.17 Multiplying and dividing decimals by whole numbers

To multiply or divide a decimal by a whole number:

- estimate the answer
- calculate the answer with a written method.

Example 1

Calculate 37.85×7

Estimate the answer: $38 \times 7 = 266$
Calculate the answer:

$$
\begin{array}{r}
37.85 \\
\times \quad\ 7 \\
\hline
264.95 \\
{\scriptstyle 5\ 5\quad 3}
\end{array}
$$

So, $37.85 \times 7 = 264.95$

Example 2

Calculate $123.68 \div 8$

Estimate the answer: $120 \div 10 = 12$
Calculate the answer:

$$
\begin{array}{r}
0\,1\,5.4\,6 \\
8\,\overline{)1^{1}2^{4}3\,.^{3}6^{4}8}
\end{array}
$$

> For your estimate, try to make your mental calculation easy. Here $120 \div 10$ is easier than $120 \div 8$.

So, $123.68 \div 8 = 15.46$

Exercise 2.17A

1 Calculate:

   a 55.8×8 **b** 45.6×9

   c 254.8×7 **d** 478.5×6

   e 765.8×7 **f** 105.8×6

   g 208.6×9 **h** 306.8×4

   i 456.8×7 **j** 568.4×9

2 Paving slabs weigh 18.62 kg each.
Find the total weight of 7 of these slabs.

3 A race track is 11.45 m long.
A car does 7 laps of the track.
How far does the car travel in total?

4 Calculate:

   a 252.8×7 **b** 34.83×6

   c 146.83×8 **d** 256.75×3

   e 256.73×5 **f** 254.88×9

   g 48.36×12 **h** 124.52×11

   i 158.56×12 **j** 136.8×15

Exercise 2.17B

1 Calculate each of these.

   a $3404.4 \div 6$ **b** $5154.4 \div 8$

   c $3834.4 \div 4$ **d** $4721.5 \div 7$

   e $5106.6 \div 9$ **f** $3941.5 \div 5$

   g $3196.2 \div 3$ **h** $9344.4 \div 6$

   i $19\,448.1 \div 7$ **j** $57\,338.4 \div 6$

2 A pack holds 6 bags of sand.
The pack weighs 78.48 kg.
Calculate the weight of one bag of sand.

3 Nine large fence panels weigh a total of 219.15 kg.
Find the weight of one fence panel.

4 Calculate:

   a $242.2 \div 7$ **b** $627.2 \div 4$

   c $1832.4 \div 6$ **d** $4186.8 \div 9$

   e $1783.8 \div 3$ **f** $5297.4 \div 9$

   g $3327.8 \div 7$ **h** $1284.5 \div 5$

   i $3737.6 \div 8$ **j** $3453.6 \div 6$

2.18 Multiplying and dividing decimals

You can use a written method to multiply or divide decimals. Remember to estimate answers each time.

Example 1

Calculate the value of 36.6×6.8

Estimate the answer: $40 \times 7 = 280$

To calculate the answer:

- write the calculation as numbers with no decimal points
- multiply in the normal way

$$
\begin{array}{r}
3\ 66 \\
\times \qquad 68 \\
\hline
2_3\,1_3 9\ 60 \\
2_5\,9_4 28 \\
\hline
2_1 4\ \ 8\ \ 88 \\
\end{array}
$$

The estimate is 280 so you have to place the decimal point between the digits of the answer to make a number close to the estimate.

With the digits 24888 we make 248.88 between 200 and 300

So, $36.6 \times 6.8 = 248.88$

Example 2

Calculate the value of $33.6 \div 1.2$

Think of this as $336 \div 12$

Estimate the answer: $300 \div 10 = 30$

Calculate the answer:
$$
\begin{array}{r}
0\,2\ 8 \\
12\overline{)33\,{}^9 6} \\
\end{array}
$$

So $33.6 \div 1.2 = 28$

You can now answer a family of decimal calculations:

As $336 \div 12 = 28$

You can say that: $33.6 \div 1.2 = 28$

and $3.36 \div 0.12 = 28$

and $0.336 \div 0.012 = 28$

and so on.

Exercise 2.18A

1 Use a written method to work out each of these.
   You must show your working.
   a 2.6 × 5.7   **b** 3.5 × 8.6   **c** 6.8 × 8.3   **d** 4.7 × 5.9
   e 7.8 × 5.4   **f** 6.7 × 1.8   **g** 5.8 × 4.7   **h** 7.4 × 5.9
   i 3.8 × 7.4   **j** 6.8 × 9.4

2 Show how you calculate each of these.
   a 3.6 × 1.8   **b** 6.4 × 7.6   **c** 6.8 × 5.7   **d** 2.4 × 5.8
   e 20.6 × 7.6   **f** 7.9 × 4.3   **g** 85.4 × 6.2   **h** 34.7 × 7.6
   i 15.6 × 3.4   **j** 25.6 × 7.5

3 Use a written method to calculate each of these.
   a 47.6 ÷ 1.4   **b** 75.4 ÷ 1.3   **c** 118.4 ÷ 1.6   **d** 110.4 ÷ 1.2
   e 185.6 ÷ 1.6   **f** 244.8 ÷ 1.8   **g** 362.1 ÷ 1.7   **h** 613.7 ÷ 1.9

4 Show how you work out each of these.
   a 46.08 ÷ 1.8   **b** 64.82 ÷ 1.4   **c** 82.42 ÷ 1.3   **d** 98.7 ÷ 1.5
   e 90.72 ÷ 1.6   **f** 123.06 ÷ 2.1   **g** 160.25 ÷ 2.5   **h** 141.7 ÷ 2.6
   i 164.84 ÷ 2.6   **j** 157.78 ÷ 2.3

Exercise 2.18B

1 Show how you work out each of these.
   a 3.4 × 1.8   **b** 3.5 × 9.4   **c** 6.8 × 6.5   **d** 6.7 × 7.8
   e 9.8 × 7.2   **f** 3.8 × 1.6   **g** 3.8 × 5.4   **h** 9.4 × 3.7

2 Show how you calculate each of these.
   a 42.6 × 2.4   **b** 66.4 × 8.1   **c** 46.8 × 7.4   **d** 66.4 × 6.7
   e 720.6 × 5.3   **f** 636.9 × 5.8   **g** 585.4 × 8.3   **h** 4006.7 × 2.8

3 Use a written method to calculate each of these.
   You must show your working.
   a 109.2 ÷ 1.4   **b** 315.9 ÷ 1.3   **c** 571.2 ÷ 1.6   **d** 899.2 ÷ 1.6
   e 70.2 ÷ 2.6   **f** 355.6 ÷ 1.4   **g** 86.55 ÷ 1.5   **h** 44.66 ÷ 1.1

4 Show how you work out each of these.
   a 41.28 ÷ 1.2   **b** 88.76 ÷ 1.4   **c** 86.32 ÷ 1.3   **d** 72.96 ÷ 1.6
   e 105.48 ÷ 1.8   **f** 103.92 ÷ 1.2   **g** 109.76 ÷ 1.4   **h** 86.24 ÷ 1.1
   i 63.36 ÷ 1.8   **j** 162 ÷ 2.5

Revision Exercise 2   *Review*

1 Round each number to the nearest 10.

    a 163   **b** 576   **c** 1024

    d 55 645   **e** 32 428   **f** 10 504   *Unit 2.1*

2 Round each number to the nearest 100.

    a 256   **b** 3058   **c** 12 453

    d 1654   **e** 50 575   **f** 10 804   *Unit 2.1*

3 Round each number to the nearest 1000.

    a 458   **b** 15 685   **c** 20 408

    d 15 681   **e** 30 407   **f** 41 504   *Unit 2.1*

4 Give an estimate for the answer to each of these.

    a 16×63 **b** 18×86 **c** 26×92 **d** 42×81 **e** 44×58

    f 59×74 **g** 78×94 **h** 28×32 **i** 44×37 **j** 75×84 *Unit 2.2*

5 Show your working for each of these questions. Find:

    a $567 + 838$ **b** $788 + 954$ **c** $81\,675 + 564$ **d** $5683 + 3887$

    e $8294 + 10\,587$ **f** $578 + 34 + 675$ **g** $896 + 78 + 593 + 4$ *Unit 2.3*

6 Show your calculation for each of these:

    a $3055 - 867$ **b** $5008 - 3759$ **c** $4000 - 1985$

    d $12\,604 - 7858$ **e** $15\,004 - 14\,785$ **f** $1\,000\,000 - 75\,284$

    g $50\,001 - 37\,284$ *Unit 2.4*

7 Show how you calculate each of these:

    a 52×46 **b** 85×67 **c** 98×36 **d** 56×73 **e** 76×58

    f 72×67 **g** 278×56 **h** 354×86 **i** 658×74 **j** 825×73 *Unit 2.5*

8 Show how you calculate each of these:

    a $1092 \div 7$ **b** $2184 \div 8$ **c** $1536 \div 6$ **d** $6750 \div 5$

    e $2304 \div 3$ **f** $5049 \div 9$ **g** $3311 \div 7$ **h** $61\,005 \div 5$ *Unit 2.6*

9 Show how you calculate each of these:

    a $180 \div 15$ **b** $224 \div 14$ **c** $216 \div 12$ **d** $264 \div 11$

    e $368 \div 16$ **f** $468 \div 18$ **g** $338 \div 13$ **h** $448 \div 14$ *Unit 2.6*

10 List the key presses for each of these calculations.

    a £15.85 + £318 + 62p   **b** £105 + 37p + £1.62   **c** 67p + £3.24 + 6p   *Unit 2.7*

11 These are the results of calculations in £s.   *Review*
What sum of money is displayed in each case?

a 3.6   **b** 7.02   **c** 0.61   **d** 0.05
e 2.08   **f** 1.87   **g** 0.01   *Unit 2.7*

12 Estimate the answer to each calculation.

a £122.60 + £39.22 + £78.61   **b** £307.56 + £49.38 + £192.67
c £12.54 × 56   **d** £3004.85 ÷ 59   *Unit 2.7*

13 Copy each calculation and put brackets in to give the answer shown.

a $7 + 4 \times 5 = 55$ **b** $12 - 3 \times 2 = 6$ **c** $56 \div 12 - 5 = 8$
d $19 - 12 \times 7 = 49$ **e** $45 \div 9 - 3 = 2$ **f** $148 - 10 \times 12 = 28$ *Unit 2.8*

14 Copy and complete each calculation.

a $(16 - 5) \times 4 =$ **b** $24 \div (8 - 5) =$ **c** $60 \div (17 - 5) =$
d $15 \times (17 - 9) =$ **e** $14 \times (21 - 6) =$ **f** $(12 - 4) \times (7 + 8) =$ *Unit 2.8*

15 Use BoDMAS to work out:

a $23 - 8 \times 2 + 5 =$ **b** $15 \times 4 - 12 \times 3 + 8 =$
c $56 \div 8 + 3 \times 4 + 1 =$ **d** $(13 + 5) \times 4 - 23 =$ *Unit 2.8*

16 Find:

a $\frac{1}{2}$ of 34   **b** $\frac{1}{5}$ of 60   **c** $\frac{1}{3}$ of 81   **d** $\frac{1}{10}$ of 130   *Unit 2.9*

17 Find:

a $\frac{3}{5}$ of 35   **b** $\frac{5}{8}$ of 56   **c** $\frac{3}{4}$ of 96   **d** $\frac{2}{3}$ of 48
e $\frac{3}{10}$ of 90   **f** $\frac{4}{5}$ of 65   **g** $\frac{3}{8}$ of 32   **h** $\frac{5}{9}$ of 72   *Unit 2.10*

18 Calculate each of these:

a 50% of £190   **b** 25% of £140   **c** 75% of £200   **d** 30% of £50
e 60% of £70   **f** 35% of £120   **g** 80% of £4000   *Unit 2.11*

19 Calculate each of these:

a 44% of £55   **b** 72% of 360 kg   **c** 24% of £360   **d** 14% of £480
e 6% of £35   **f** 4% of £1425   **g** 32% of 420 km   **h** 85% of £46   *Unit 2.12*

20 2600 people live in Benton.
42% of them own a car.

a How many people own a car?
b What percentage don't own a car?   *Unit 2.13*

21 Last year 14 700 cars used a ferry crossing.
54% of the cars travelled on a return ticket.
How many cars was this?

Review

Unit 2.13

22 Divide:
   a £65 in the ratio 2:3   **b** £126 in the ratio 1:5
   c £104 in the ratio 5:3   **d** £308 in the ratio 5:9
   e £48 in the ratio 4:5:7   **f** £270 in the ratio 3:7:8

Unit 2.14

23 Three cyclists take part in a race.
Jaz, Joe and Kim complete distances in the ratio 5:7:4
Joe cycles 175 km. How far do Jaz and Kim each cycle?

Unit 2.14

24 Round each of these to the nearest integer.
   a 157.82   **b** 104.498   **c** 305.169
   d 575.388   **e** 5785.55

Unit 2.15

25 Estimate the answer to each of these by first rounding to the nearest integer.
   a 4.6×12.4 **b** 6.4×21.35 **c** 8.82×13.85
   d 16.56×12.72 **e** 24.72×43.8 **f** 75.27×9.85
   g 64.8×9.87 **h** 56.45×11.65

Unit 2.15

26 Estimate the answer to each of these by first rounding to the nearest integer.
   a $44.6 \div 9.42$ **b** $66.4 \div 11.35$ **c** $84.2 \div 20.65$
   d $15.56 \div 8.44$ **e** $95.72 \div 16.38$ **f** $72.27 \div 5.57$
   g $64.8 \div 12.87$ **h** $56.45 \div 7.65$

Unit 2.15

27 Use a written method to work out:
   a $56.4 + 67.8$ **b** $135.6 + 72.7$ **c** $82.9 + 56.5$
   d $9.62 + 34.7$ **e** $127.67 + 88.4$ **f** $45.76 + 18.92$
   g $30.04 + 57.2$ **h** $157.82 + 762.088$

Unit 2.16

28 Use a written method to work out:
   a $56.4 - 38.8$ **b** $135.6 - 98.7$ **c** $82.9 - 56.6$
   d $96.2 - 34.7$ **e** $127.67 - 88.7$ **f** $457.6 - 18.92$
   g $300.4 - 57.38$ **h** $657.82 - 562.088$

Unit 2.16

29 Calculate each of these.
   a 56×8 **b** 45×9 **c** 24×7 **d** 186.7×8
   e 246.7×5 **f** 905.7×8 **g** 1034.67×5 **h** 34.65×7
   i 673.8×3

Unit 2.17

30 Calculate each of these: *Review*

    a 2650.2 ÷ 7   **b** 217 448 ÷ 4   **c** 25 253.6 ÷ 8   **d** 5893.2 ÷ 9

    e 34 567.5 ÷ 5   **f** 33 856.8 ÷ 6   **g** 31 456.5 ÷ 5   **h** 38 245.9 ÷ 7

    i 45 188.8 ÷ 8

                                                                            Unit 2.17

31 Show how you calculate each of these.

    a 2.8 × 5.6   **b** 7.5 × 4.8   **c** 8.6 × 9.4   **d** 6.3 × 8.4

    e 12.7 × 5.4   **f** 18.2 × 5.6   **g** 56.4 × 2.8   **h** 34.7 × 8.6

    i 45.7 × 3.5   **j** 78.4 × 5.6

                                                                             Unit 2.18

32 Show how you calculate each of these.

    a 54.04 ÷ 1.4   **b** 677.64 ÷ 1.2   **c** 370.05 ÷ 1.5   **d** 875.52 ÷ 1.6

    e 843.05 ÷ 1.3   **f** 903.68 ÷ 1.6   **g** 461.52 ÷ 1.8   **h** 619.84 ÷ 1.3

    i 3700.65 ÷ 1.5   **j** 583.52 ÷ 1.6

                                                                             Unit 2.18

Investigation

Multiplication puzzle

This is a multiplication puzzle that uses only the digits
1, 2, 3, 4 and 5:

This puzzle shows 123 × 45

This puzzle shows 412 × 53

1   What is the answer for each of the puzzles shown?

Change the numbers in the multiplication puzzle yourself.
Remember you can only use the digits 1, 2, 3, 4, and 5.

2   What is your new multiplication?

3   What is your new answer?

Change the numbers again still using the digits 1, 2, 3, 4
and 5.

4   What is the biggest answer you can make?

5   What is the smallest answer you can make?

3 EQUATIONS, FORMULAE AND IDENTITIES

3.1 Substituting in formulae

A formula links variables so you can use it for different values.
A formula can be given in words or in symbols.

> A **variable** is a quantity that can change.

Example 1

The charge for film processing is worked out in this way:

£2 to develop the film and 18 p for each print.

> This is a formula given in words.

Calculate the charge to process a film with 24 prints.

$$\text{Charge} = £2 + (24 \times 18\,\text{p})$$
$$= £2 + £4.32$$
$$= £6.32$$

> Remember 18 p is keyed into a calculator as 0.18 if you want the answer in £s.

So, the charge to process this film with 24 prints is £6.32.

Example 2

The area of a rectangle is given by the formula $A = l \times w$

Find the area of a rectangle where: $l = 18\,\text{cm}, \quad w = 9\,\text{cm}$

$$A = l \times w$$
$$= 18 \times 9$$
$$A = 162$$

> Remember area is given in square units.

So, the area of the rectangle is $162\,\text{cm}^2$.

Exercise 3.1A

1 Hire charges for a village hall is worked out in this way:
     £35 plus £8.75 for each hour of the hire.
   Calculate the charge to hire this hall for:
   a 5 hours   **b** 9 hours   **c** 24 hours

2 A removal company charges in this way:
     £375 plus 15 p for each mile travelled.
   Calculate the removal charge for each of these:
   a 82 miles   **b** 364 miles   **c** 672 miles

3 The formula for the area A of a rectangle is: $A = l \times w$
Calculate the area of a rectangle with:
a length l of 12.4 cm and a width w of 8 cm.

4 The formula for the perimeter P of a rectangle is:

$P = 2l + 2w$ where l is the length and w the width.

Use the formula to complete this table:

Rectangle	l cm	w cm	$2l$	$2w$	P cm
a	15	12	30	24	54
b	8.5	6.5	☐	☐	☐
c	57	22.8	☐	☐	☐

> Remember $2l$ stands for $2 \times l$

5 A formula that links v, u and t is: $v = 3u - 2t$
Use the formula to calculate:

> Remember ft stands for $f \times t$

a a value for v when: $u = 3$ and $t = 2$
b a value for v when: $u = 20$ and $t = 15$
c a value for v when: $u = 0$ and $t = 24$

Exercise 3.1B

1 A house painter makes these charges:
   £175 plus £35 for each window.
Calculate the charge for painting:

a a house with 15 windows
b a bungalow with 9 windows
c a block of flats with 52 windows

2 The formula for the area A of a triangle is:
$A = 0.5 \times b \times h$
Copy and complete this table:

Triangle	b cm	h cm	A cm^2
ABC	9	17	☐
KLM	17	21	☐
RST	15	15	☐

3 This formula is used to work out car hire charges £C:

$$C = 25d + 0.35m$$

where d is the number of days
and m is the number of miles.

Copy and complete this table.

Hire	Number of days	Number of miles	Charge £s
a	4	356	☐
b	9	835	☐
c	15	2086	☐

3.2 Constructing simple formulae

You can construct simple algebraic formulae from the data
for a situation.

You need to think about how one number depends on
another number.

You use letters to stand for amounts that vary.

Example

This is a simple rule used by some people.

> To make good tea use one tea bag for each person
> and one for the pot.

Write the rule as a formula with letters.

The number of tea bags depends on the number of people.

To write the formula in letters:

Let t stand for the number of tea bags
and p stand for the number of people

    The formula is: $t = p + 1$

Remember:
A formula is a rule that
you can use to work
something out.

The number of tea bags
and people can vary.
They are the variables.

Exercise 3.2A

1   Asa buys cards to send to players in his hockey club.
    He uses this rule to work out the number of cards to buy:

    One for each player and 85 extra.

    Write this rule as a formula using letters.
    (Let *c* stand for the number of cards and *p* for the
    number of players.)

2   This rule is used to work out the number of sandwiches
    to give to a group of people.

    The number of sandwiches is two per person
    plus three.

    Write this rule as a formula with letters.
    (Let *s* stand for sandwiches and *p* stand for people.)

3   For the number of people on a car ferry this rule is used:

    The number of people is 3 per car plus 165 extra.

    Write this as a formula with letters.
    (Use *p* for people and *c* for cars.)

4   For the amount of cable needed to fix telephones in an
    office, fitters use this rule:

    The cable needed is 12 metres for each phone
    and 50 metres extra.

    Write this as a formula with letters.
    (Use the letters *c* and *t*.)

5   Anya makes jeans.
    She uses this rule to work out how many rivets to buy for
    each order.

    The number of rivets is 11 for each pair of jeans
    plus 120 extra.

    Write the rule as a formula with letters.
    (Use *r* and *j*).

Exercise 3.2B

1 A supermarket uses this rule for the number of plastic bags it uses in a day:

   The number of bags is 5 for each customer plus 350 extra.

   Write the rule as a formula with the letters b and c.

Each time, think about the letters you will use in your formula.

2 A milkman uses this rule for the number of bottles to load on his van:

   The number of bottles is 4 for each house plus 35 for other sales.

   a Write this rule as a formula with letters. Use the letters b and h.
   b Use your rule to work out how many bottles to load for 161 houses.

3 Hi-Way markings uses this rule for the number of litres of white line paint it needs for each job:

   The amount of paint is 12 litres per mile of road plus 15 litres.

   a Write this rule as a formula with letters p and m.
   b Use your formula to calculate how much paint is needed for 56 miles of road.

4 A firm that makes greenhouses uses this rule to calculate the number of clips to pack in a kit:

   The number of clips is 5 per pane of glass plus 12 clips per kit.

   a Write this rule as a formula with the letters c and p.
   b Use your formula to calculate the number of clips in a Yeoman kit.
   The Yeoman greenhouse has 18 panes of glass.

3.3 Balance puzzles

▶ To solve these puzzles try to find a way to add weights or take weights off so that you get the mystery object balanced with a weight.

Exercise 3.3A

Find the mystery weights in each diagram.

1 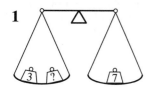   **2**    **3**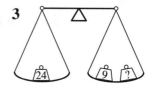

4 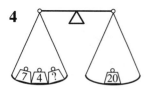   **5**    **6**

7    **8**    **9**

Exercise 3.3B

Find the unknown weights. Where there is more than one unknown weight in a question, these weights are equal.

1 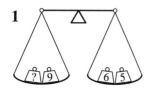   **2**    **3**

4    **5**    **6**

7    **8**    **9**

3.4 Solving an equation by balancing

▶ You can think of an equation like a balance.
The $=$ sign is the balance point.

Example 1

Solve the equation $d + 4 = 9$

As a balance it looks like this:

If you take 4 **from both sides**
it will still balance.

$$d + 4 - 4 = 9 - 4$$

So the value of d is 5.
We can say that $d = 5$

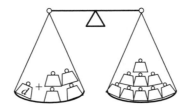

Example 2

Solve $3x + 5 = 11$

As a balance it looks like this:

Stage 1:   Take 5 **from both sides**.

$$3x + 5 - 5 = 11 - 5$$

So $\qquad 3x = 6$

Stage 2:   Divide **both sides** by 3.

$$3x \div 3 = 6 \div 3$$

So $\qquad x = 2$

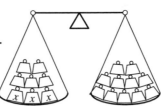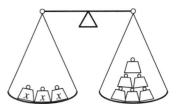

Exercise 3.4A

1 a Draw a balance for the equation $g + 5 = 11$.
  b What must you take from both sides to get g on its own?
  c What value balances g?

2 Use balances to solve these equations.

  a $h + 3 = 12$ **b** $v + 6 = 9$ **c** $f + 4 = 10$
  d $k + 8 = 22$ **e** $y + 15 = 44$ **f** $w + 18 = 35$
  g $v + 18 = 54$ **h** $d + 21 = 94$ **i** $k + 32 = 105$

3 Solve these equations.

  a $d + 7 = 22$ **b** $s + 21 = 40$ **c** $10 + t = 28$
  d $y + 11 = 41$ **e** $35 + h = 90$ **f** $k + 56 = 60$
  g $12 + d = 71$ **h** $p + 121 = 175$ **i** $w + 65 = 5000$

4 Solve these equations in two stages.

    a Solve $2w + 4 = 26$

    b Solve $3k + 5 = 26$

    c Solve $5d + 8 = 23$

> **Remember:**
> At each stage you must do the same thing **to both sides**.

Exercise 3.4B

1 Solve these equations.

    a $w + 5 = 22$ **b** $15 + y = 66$ **c** $12 + k = 75$

    d $y + 18 = 40$ **e** $55 + h = 100$ **f** $105 + p = 250$

    g $t + 34 = 79$ **h** $56 + d = 101$ **i** $78 + b = 222$

2 Solve these equations in two stages.

    a $2x + 5 = 11$ **b** $2z + 1 = 17$ **c** $3s + 7 = 28$

    d $3k + 5 = 35$ **e** $3y + 12 = 27$ **f** $4g + 8 = 52$

    g $5y + 2 = 37$ **h** $12k + 1 = 61$ **i** $9d + 3 = 57$

3 Solve these equations.

    a $h + 6 = 16$ **b** $7 + k = 42$ **c** $4 + f = 40$

    d $4 + s = 39$ **e** $3q + 8 = 11$ **f** $8 + 4w = 88$

    g $3q + 6 = 27$ **h** $6 + r = 6$ **i** $6p + 54 = 120$

4 Find a value for d if $6 + 5d = 41$.

Equations may have minus signs.

▶ A balance is not as obvious for an equation with a minus sign.

▶ You must remember to **do the same thing to both sides**.

Example 3

Solve the equation $p - 4 = 12$.

Add 4 to both sides $p - 4 + 4 = 12 + 4$

so $p = 16$

> You add 4 to both sides to cancel out the -4 because
> $-4 + 4 = 0$

Example 4

Solve the equation $3d - 6 = 18$.

Add 6 to both sides $3d - 6 + 6 = 18 + 6$

so $3d = 24$

Divide both sides by 3 $3d \div 3 = 24 \div 3$

so $d = 8$

> **Remember:**
> Always check your answer:
> $3 \times 8 - 6 = 24 - 6 = 18$

Exercise 3.4C

1 **a** To solve $d - 5 = 7$ what must you do to both sides?
   b Solve the equation.

2 Solve each of these equations. Say what you do each time.
   a $t - 7 = 15$ **b** $y - 2 = 12$ **c** $b - 5 = 7$
   d $f - 24 = 56$ **e** $w - 53 = 173$ **f** $k - 9 = 14$

3 Solve these equations. Show all the stages.
   a $2d - 2 = 8$ **b** $5f - 3 = 12$ **c** $4e - 10 = 26$
   d $5s - 10 = 0$ **e** $6w - 2 = 58$ **f** $7x - 6 = 43$
   g $5q - 3 = 52$ **h** $3e - 8 = 25$ **i** $20y - 4 = 96$

Exercise 3.4D

1 Solve these equations.
   a $r - 74 = 185$ **b** $y - 37 = 43$ **c** $17 = x - 5$

   > **Hint:**
   > $17 = x - 5$ is the same as
   > $x - 5 = 17$

   d $w - 8 = 53$ **e** $k - 13 = 31$ **f** $y - 21 = 44$
   g $t - 14 = 56$ **h** $1 = y - 35$ **i** $w - 1 = 1$

2 Solve each of these equations.
   a $3x - 7 = 29$ **b** $5a - 20 = 80$ **c** $18 = 6s - 12$
   d $2f - 8 = 0$ **e** $5x - 7 = 103$ **f** $4w - 8 = 20$
   g $7q - 21 = 63$ **h** $6d - 17 = 67$ **i** $5a - 14 = 26$

3 Solve each of these mixed equations showing each stage.
   a $s + 4 = 19$ **b** $5 = y - 8$ **c** $x - 13 = 27$ **d** $6d - 4 = 56$
   e $11 = 2s + 3$ **f** $32 = 4g - 4$ **g** $t + 7 = 103$ **h** $7v - 2 = 47$
   i $0 = r - 48$ **j** $15 = 6t + 9$ **k** $5t + 4 = 124$ **l** $56 = 7r - 7$

3.5 Collecting like terms

▶ $3x + 4y - 6z$ is an algebraic expression:

each part is called a **term**.

Like terms use exactly the same letters:

$3a$ and $6a$ are like terms

$4a$ and $3ab$ are *not* like terms

You can simplify an expression by collecting like terms.

Example 1

Collect like terms to simplify this expression:
$5a + 4c + 3a - 2c$

Two terms have the variable a, and two terms have the variable c.

$$5a + 4c + 3a - 2c = 8a + 2c$$
(Combine the terms in a, and the terms in c.)

Example 2

Collect like terms to simplify: $6ab + 5y - 2ab + y$

Remember y is the same as $1y$.

$$6ab + 5y - 2ab + y = 4ab + 6y$$
(You treat ab as one letter.)

When you collect like terms you **simplify** the expression.

Exercise 3.5A

1 Collect like terms to simplify each expression.

a $5y + 3y + y + 3y$

b $3c + 7c + c + 4c$

c $12y + 4y + 5a + 9a$

d $5b + 3x - 3b + 2x$

e $x + y + 2y + x$

f $4v - v + 2b - b$

2 Collect like terms and simplify each expression.

a $5ay + 3ax + ay - ax$

b $17bc + 3ax + bc - 4ax$

c $5h - 6h + 3xy + h - xy$

d $8k - 5v + 2v + k + 9v$

Exercise 3.5B

1 Collect like terms in each of these expressions.

a $4x + 5y + 3x + y$

b $7c + 4h + 9h - 2c$

c $8y + x + 3y + 5x - y$

d $11y + 12x + y - 5x$

2 Collect like terms in each of these expressions.

a $7x + 5y + 3y - 4x + 5x$

b $8t + 5b + y - b - 13t + 6y$

c $12y + 4cv - 7y + cv$

d $5x + 3ac + x + 2ac - 6x$

3 Copy and complete:

a $5y + 6x + \boxed{} + 5x = 11x + 7y$

b $3cx + 5y - cx + \boxed{} = 2cx + 6y$

Revision Exercise 3

Review

1 A formula that links v, u and t is: $v = 4u + 2t$
   a find a value for v when: $u = 4$ and $t = 5$
   b find a value for v when: $u = 7$ and $t = 3$
   c find a value for v when: $u = 12$ and $t = 0$ *Unit 3.1*

2 For the number of chairs in an office this rule is used:
   The number of chairs is 2 chairs for each desk plus 3.
   Write this as a formula with letters.
   [use the letters c and d]   *Unit 3.2*

3 This rule is used for the number of parking spaces:
   The number of spaces is two less than the number
   of people in an office multiplied by three.
   Write this as a formula with letters.
   [use s for parking spaces and p for people]   *Unit 3.2*

4 A firm that makes sheds uses this rule to work out
   the number of nails to pack in a kit:
   The number of nails is 24 per panel plus 10 per kit.
   a Write this rule as a formula with letters.
   The *York* shed has 15 panels.
   b Use your formula to calculate the number of nails in the *York* kit.   *Unit 3.2*

5 Find the mystery weights in each diagram
   a   **b**

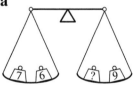   

   c   **d**

   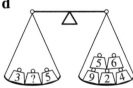   *Unit 3.3*

6 Solve these equations.
   a $y + 9 = 14$ **b** $k + 8 = 23$ **c** $9 + y = 46$
   d $x + 18 = 54$ **e** $h + 22 = 73$ **f** $65 + y = 81$ *Unit 3.4*

7 Solve these equations.   *Review*

    a $y - 8 = 14$ **b** $k - 14 = 23$ **c** $y - 18 = 46$

    d $x - 54 = 54$ **e** $h - 35 = 73$ **f** $y - 25 = 81$ *Unit 3.4*

8 Solve: $45 = 23 + m$ *Unit 3.4*

9 Collect like terms to simplify each expression.

    a $3x + 4y + 2x + 5y$ **b** $5x - 3y + 2x + 8y$

    c $9y - 5x + y + 12x$ **d** $7x + y + x + 2y$

    e $16x - 4y + x + 10y$ **f** $3a + b + 2c + 3a + b - c$

    g $15a + 3b - 4c + 2b + 5c - 4a$ **h** $12a + 3x - 5y + 2x + 5a + 9y$

    i $4ax + 5ay + ay - 2ax$ *Unit 3.5*

10 A removal company charges in this way:

    £275 + 18p for each mile travelled.

    Calculate the removal charge for each of these:

    a 256 miles   **b** 675 miles   **c** 1256 miles   *Unit 3.5*

Investigation

Short shuffle

1 Look at the diagram on the right. What is the smallest number of moves you need to sort the counters so that the patterns are together?

> From this
> ● ○ ● ○ ● ○ ● ○ ● ○
> To this
> ● ● ● ○ ○ ○

2 What about shuffling 4 of each type, 5 of each type etc.?

3 Write a rule for the number of moves for any number of each type.

4 GRAPHS

4.1 Coordinates

You can fix the position of any point on a grid using two
numbers called **coordinates**. Coordinates are written (x, y)

The axes are:

distance along x-axis   distance along y-axis

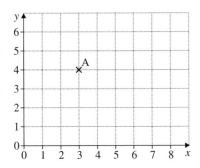

The coordinates of A are (3, 4)

> One way to remember
> the order of coordinates
> is: along the passage and
> up the stairs.

Exercise 4.1A

1 Give the coordinates of each point.

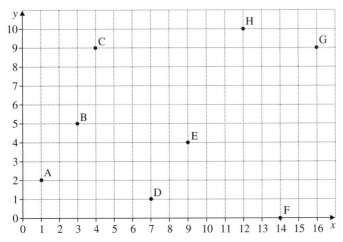

2 Draw a grid with values of x from 0 to 10 and values of
  y from 0 to 10.
  On your grid plot and label these points:
  A(2, 5), B(4, 7), C(9, 2), D(8, 0), E(9, 9),
  F(3, 4), G(7, 4), H(0, 3), I(6, 5), J(5, 6)

Exercise 4.1B

1 Give the coordinates of each point.

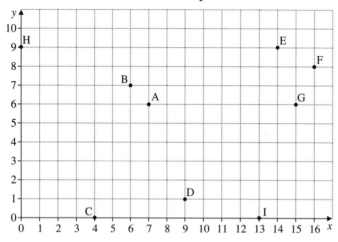

2 Draw a grid with values of x from 0 to 8 and values of y from 0 to 8.

On your grid draw a shape that has 8 edges. Label your shape A, B, C, D, E, F, G, H.

List each corner of your shape and give its coordinates.

4.2 Coordinates in the four quadrants

The x-axis and the y-axis can also show negative values.

Example 1

Give the coordinates of each vertex of the shape ABCDEF.

> Think of a vertex as a corner of a 2-D shape.

Vertex	Coordinate
A	(⁻1, 3)
B	(1, 3)
C	(2, 2)
D	(2, ⁻2)
E	(0, ⁻2)
F	(⁻2, 1)

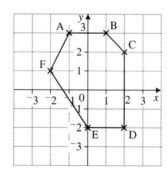

The negative signs are important.

Remember the points (2, 3) and (⁻2, 3) are different.

Exercise 4.2A

1 Give the coordinates of each point.

a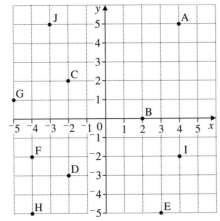

b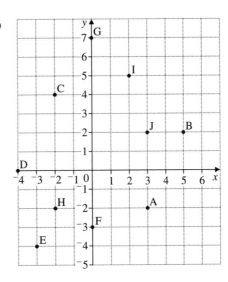

Exercise 4.2B

1 Give the coordinates of each point.

a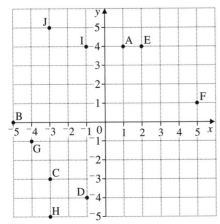

b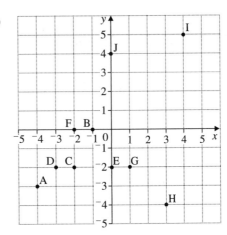

Exercise 4.2C

1 Plot these points and join them in order.

A(3, 0), B(2, ⁻3), C(1, ⁻1), D(⁻2, ⁻1), F(1, 1), G(2, 3)

Draw axes like the ones in the example.

2 **a** Plot each of these points on a pair of axes and join them in order.

   A(⁻3, 0), B(⁻2, 3), C(0, 1), D(2, 4), E(3, 0),
   F(2, ⁻4), G(0, ⁻1), H(⁻2, ⁻3)

   b How many edges has your shape?

3 **a** Plot each of these points on a pair of axes and join them in order.

   A(0, 5), B(3, 2), C(2, 2), D(2, ⁻4), E(0, ⁻3),
   F(⁻2, ⁻4), G(⁻2, 2), H(⁻3, 2)

   b Join C to F and G to D. Give the coordinates where CF and GD cross.

4 **a** Plot each of these points on a pair of axes and join them in order.

   A(⁻4, ⁻3), B(⁻4, ⁻1), C(⁻1.5, 2), D(1, ⁻1), E(1, ⁻3)

   b Join A to D and B to E. Give the coordinates where AD and BE cross.

   c Join A to C. Give the coordinates where AC and BD cross.

   d Give the coordinates of the midpoint of AE.

5 ABCD is a square with coordinates:

   A(⁻1, 3), B(3, 3), C(☐, ☐), D(⁻1, ⁻1)

   a Give the co-ordinates of C.

   WXYZ are the midpoints of AB, BC, CD, and DA.

   b Give the coordinates of W, X, Y, and Z.

Exercise 4.2D _____

1 **a** Plot these points and join them in order.

   A(0, ⁻2), B(⁻1, ⁻3), C(⁻1, 1), D(⁻2, 1), E(0, 3),
   F(2, 1), G(1, 1), H(1, ⁻3)

   b How many edges has your shape?

   Draw axes like the ones in the example.

2 a Plot each of these points on a pair of axes and join them in order.

A(¯2, 4), B(2, 1), C(5, 0), D(2, ¯1), E(¯2, ¯4), F(¯4, ¯2), G(¯4, 2)

Join A to E, G to D, and B to F.

b Give the coordinates where, GD and FB cross.

c Give the coordinates where AE crosses GD, and where it crosses FB.

d Give the coordinates of the midpoint of AG.

3 a Plot each of these points on a pair of axes and join them in order.

A(¯4, 2), B(¯3, 6), C(2, 5), D(4, 2), E(3, ¯2), F(¯4, ¯4)

b Join B to E and A to D. Give the coordinates where BE and AD cross.

c Give the coordinates of the midpoint of DF.

d Join A to C. Give the coordinates where BE and AC cross.

e Which other diagonal of the shape goes through the point (2, 0)?

4 a Plot each of these points on a pair of axes and join them in order.

A(¯4, 0), B(¯2, 0), C(¯1, ¯1), D(2, ¯1), E(3, ¯2), F(2, ¯4), G(1, ¯3), H(¯2, ¯3), I(¯3, ¯2), J(¯5, ¯2)

b Join D to H and C to D. Give the coordinates where DH and CD cross.

c Join A to I and, B to J. Give the coordinates where AI and BJ cross.

5 a Plot these points and join them in order.

A(¯2, 2), B(1, 3), C(3, 3), D(4, 0), E(3, ¯3), F(1, ¯3), G(¯2, ¯2)

b Join B to F and G to C.

c Give the coordinates where BF and GC cross.

d Join B to D.

e Give the coordinates where BD and GC cross.

f BF crosses a line at (1, ¯1). What is the line? (You may have to draw the line.)

Revision Exercise 4

Review

1 Give the coordinates of each point.

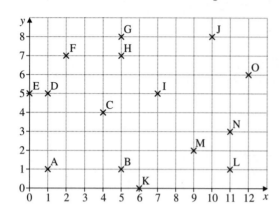

Unit 4.1

2 Give the coordinates of each point.

a

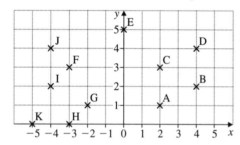

b

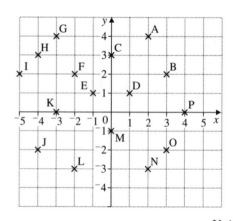

Unit 4.2

3 a Plot each point on a pair of axes and join them in order.

(2, 7) (5, 2) (5, ⁻2) (2, ⁻2) (⁻2, ⁻2) (⁻5, ⁻3) (⁻4, 1) (⁻6, 5) (⁻3, 7)

b How many edges has your shape?

Unit 4.2

4 ABCD is a rectangle with coordinates:

A(⁻4, 5) B(4, 5) C(4, ⁻2) D(•, •)

a What are the coordinates of the point D?

Unit 4.2

K, L, M and N are the mid-points of AB, BC, CD and AD.

b Give the coordinates of K, L, M and N.

Unit 4.2

5 GEOMETRICAL REASONING

5.1 Angles and turns

▶ There are 360° in a full turn.
The symbol ° means degrees.

To find a fraction of a full turn multiply the fraction by 360°.

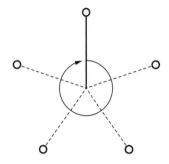

Example
What is $\frac{3}{8}$ of a full turn in degrees?

To find $\frac{3}{8}$ of 360° multiply 360 by 3 then divide the answer by 8

$$360 \times 3 = 1080$$
$$1080 \div 8 = 135$$

So, $\frac{3}{8}$ of a full turn is 135°

▶ For any turn you should give the direction.

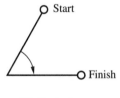

60° Clockwise

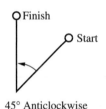

45° Anticlockwise

Exercise 5.1A

1 Find each of these turns in degrees.
   a Half a full turn   **b** $\frac{1}{4}$ of a full turn

   c $\frac{3}{4}$ of a full turn   **d** $\frac{1}{5}$ of a full turn

   e $\frac{3}{5}$ of a full turn   **f** $\frac{1}{8}$ of a full turn

   g $\frac{2}{3}$ of a full turn   **h** $\frac{5}{6}$ of a full turn

   i $\frac{4}{9}$ of a full turn   **j** $\frac{5}{8}$ of a full turn

2 Think of compass directions.
Face North then turn clockwise to face West.
What fraction of a full turn did you make?

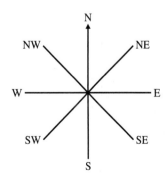

3 Face North then turn anticlockwise to face West.
What fraction of a full turn did you make?

4 Face North then turn to face South.

    a What fraction of a full turn did you make?

    b What direction did you turn?

    c What other turn could you have made?

Exercise 5.1B _____

1 Give each of these turns in degrees.

    a $\frac{5}{8}$ of a full turn   **b** $\frac{4}{5}$ of a full turn   **c** $\frac{2}{3}$ of a full turn   **d** $\frac{5}{6}$ of a full turn

    e $\frac{9}{10}$ of a full turn   **f** $\frac{8}{15}$ of a full turn   **g** $\frac{3}{10}$ of a full turn   **h** $\frac{1}{4}$ of a full turn

    i $\frac{5}{12}$ of a full turn   **j** $\frac{1}{30}$ of a full turn

2 Face North then turn clockwise to face North East.
What fraction of a full turn did you make?

3 Face North then turn clockwise to face South West.
What fraction of a full turn did you make?

4 Give each clockwise turn in degrees.

    a Face N. Turn to face W.   **b** Face S. Turn to face W.

    c Face N. Turn to face E.   **d** Face W. Turn to face E.

    e Face W. Turn to face N.   **f** Face S. Turn to face E.

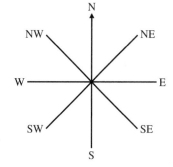

5.2 Compass bearings

You can give or fix positions using the points of the compass.
You need to give the direction and the distance from the centre.

A magnetic compass points at Magnetic North. This is not the same as True North (the North Pole).

Example

The map shows the area around a train station.

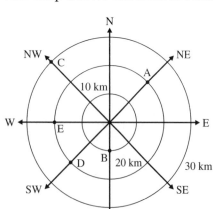

A Cinema
B Football ground
C Motorway junction
D Golf course
E Hypermarket

What is at the following places?

a 10 km South   **b** 30 km North West

c 20 km South West   **d** 20 km West

> The railway station is at the centre of the map.

a 10 km South is a football ground

b 30 km North West is a motorway junction

c 20 km South West is a golf course

d 20 km West is a hypermarket

> Each gap between the rings on the map stands for 10 km.

Exercise 5.2A

1 Copy and complete this table for the radar below.

Letter	Location	Letter	Location
A	☐	B	☐
C	☐	☐	40 km SE
☐	20 km NW	H	☐
U	☐	P	☐
G	☐	☐	30 km S
T	☐	☐	20 km SW

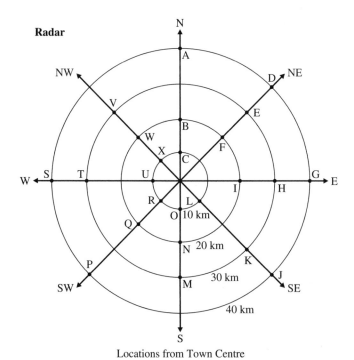

Locations from Town Centre

Exercise 5.2B

1 Copy and complete this table for the radar on page 101.

Letter	Location	Letter	Location
F	☐	O	☐
☐	20 km S	☐	30 km NE
D	☐	☐	10 km SE
X	☐	☐	20 km E
K	☐	☐	30 km NW
R	☐	☐	40 km W

5.3 Bearings

You can fix a position using a bearing and a
distance from the centre.
A bearing is a direction measured from North
in a clockwise direction.
North is 000°.

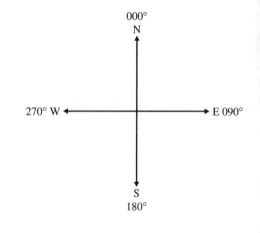

The simple compass has these directions and
bearings.

Other directions can be put in.

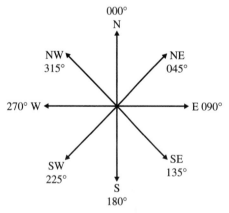

The best way to draw and measure bearings is with an angle
measurer.

- First draw in a North line.
- Then measure around clockwise to the bearing.

Exercise 5.3A _____

1 Copy and complete this table for the diagram shown.
   All bearings and distances are from **P**.

Location	Bearing	Distance
A	☐	☐
B	☐	☐
C	☐	☐
D	☐	☐
E	☐	☐
F	☐	☐
G	☐	☐
H	☐	☐

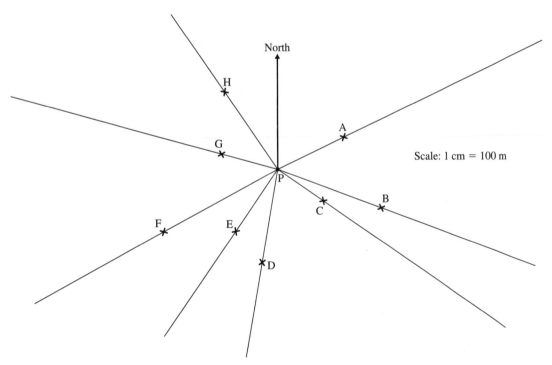

Scale: 1 cm = 100 m

2 Give the bearing of each of these directions.
   a East   **b** South West   **c** North East   **d** West

3 An aircraft starts a journey on a bearing of 135°, then
   alters course to fly at 180° to its previous bearing.
   On what course is it now travelling?

Exercise 5.3B

1 The diagram shows the journey of an aircraft flying from
A to B.
The diagram uses a scale of 1 cm = 10 km.

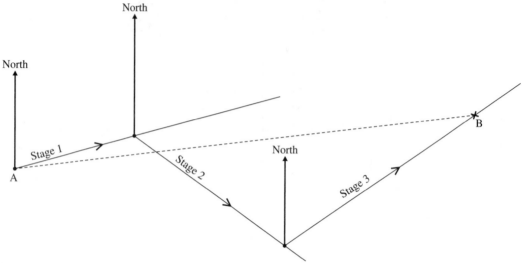

   a Find the bearing and distance for Stage 1.
   b Stage 2 was 50 km long. What is its bearing?
   c Find the bearing and distance for Stage 3 of the flight.

Imagine the aircraft flew from A to B in a straight line.

   d How far is it from A to B? Give your answer to the
   nearest 10 km.
   e Find the bearing from A to B.

2 The diagram shows the position of four fishing boats.

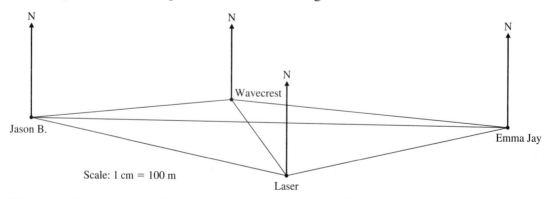

From each boat, give the bearing and distance of the
other three boats.

5.4 Types of angles

▶ Angles are grouped into three types.

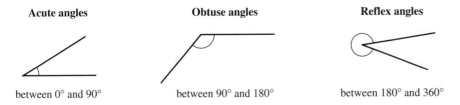

Acute angles	Obtuse angles	Reflex angles
between 0° and 90°	between 90° and 180°	between 180° and 360°

Exercise 5.4A

1 For each angle say if it is obtuse, acute or reflex.

    a 154°   **b** 212°   **c** 43°

    d 88°   **e** 312°   **f** 190°

2 Say if each angle is acute, obtuse or reflex.

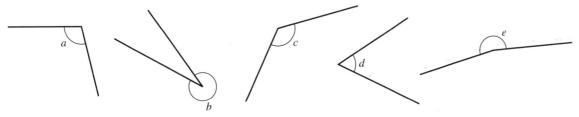

3 Two angles A and B make up a full turn.
Describe the types of angle B can be if:

    a A is acute   **b** A is obtuse   **c** A is reflex

Exercise 5.4B

1 a Draw and label an obtuse angle.

   b Draw and label a reflex angle.

   c Draw and label acute angle.

2 Which of these angles is acute?

      85°   122°   255°   104°   76°   22°

3 Can a triangle have two obtuse interior angles?
Explain your answer.

4 Is this statement sometimes true, always true or never
true? 'Half a reflex angle is an obtuse angle'.

5.5 Estimating and measuring angles

▶ To measure an angle accurately use a protractor or angle measurer.
Decide whether to use the clockwise or the anticlockwise scale.

▶ Estimate the size of an angle first, before you measure it.
To estimate an angle:

- Compare it with a right angle (90°) – is it smaller or larger?

- Compare it with a straight line (180°).

- Compare it with an angle of 270°.

Exercise 5.5A _____

Look at these angles.

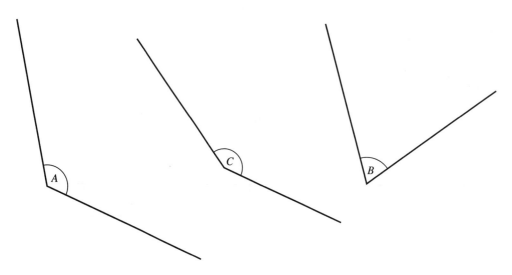

1 a Is angle *A* greater or smaller than 90°?
  b Is angle *A* greater or smaller than 180°?
  c Estimate the size of angle *A* in degrees.
  d Measure angle *A* accurately.

2 For angle *B* and angle *C*:
  a estimate its size
  b measure its size accurately.

3 Estimate then measure accurately the size of these angles.

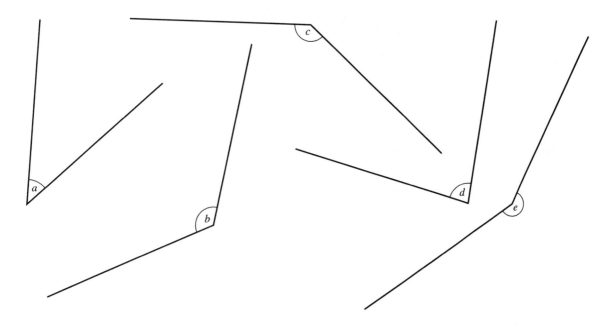

Exercise 5.5B

1 Measure accurately the size of each of these angles.

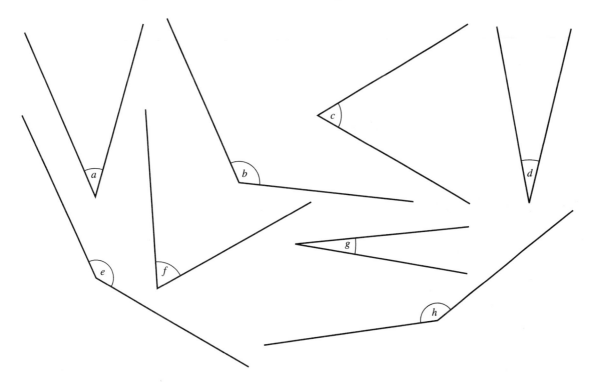

2 a What should the interior angles of a triangle total?
  b Measure the sizes of each angle in this triangle.
  c Calculate the total of the three angles.

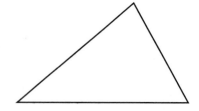

3 a Measure each interior angle in this shape.
  b Find the total of the four interior angles.

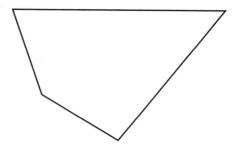

4 A right-angled triangle has sides with the lengths shown.
  a Draw the triangle accurately.
  b Measure the two angles x and y.

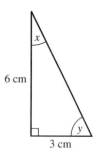

5.6 Drawing angles

▶ To draw an angle of 100°:

| Draw a straight line: | Position your protractor correctly: | Mark the angle 100°. Start from 0. | Join the mark. Label the angle. |

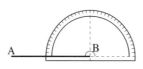

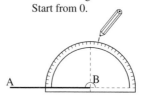

Exercise 5.6A

1 Without measuring, estimate and sketch these angles.

    a 45°   **b** 60°   **c** 90°   **d** 110°   **e** 200°   **f** 310°

    Now measure to check your estimates.

2 Accurately draw these angles:

    a 48°   **b** 156°   **c** 94°

    d 170°   **e** 145°   **f** 17°

    g 112°   **h** 138°   **i** 99°

Exercise 5.6B

1 Without measuring, estimate and draw these angles.

    a 150°   **b** 20°   **c** 200°

    d 340°   **e** 280°   **f** 310°

    Now measure to check your estimates.

2 Draw these angles accurately.

    a 73°   **b** 173°   **c** 273°

    d 118°   **e** 214°   **f** 146°

    g 19°   **h** 341°   **i** 154°

    j 206°   **k** 83°   **l** 277°

    m 345°   **n** 15°   **o** 264°

3 Mike drew an angle of 134°.

    Kelly measured it and found it to be only 46°.

    What had Mike done wrong?

5.7 Angles on a straight line and at a point

▶ The angles on a straight line add up to 180°.

Example 1

Calculate the size of angle *a*.

You know that $34° + a = 180°$

So $a = 180° - 34°$

                      $a = 146°$

▶ Angles at a point add up to 360°.

Example 2

Calculate the size of angle b.

You know that $b + 90° + 124° = 360°$

So $b = 360° - 214°$

                                      $b = 146°$

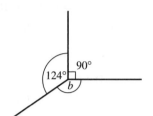

Exercise 5.7A _____

1 Calculate each labelled angle.

a   **b**   **c**   **d**   **e**

2 Calculate each labelled angle.

a   **b** 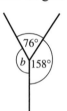   **c**   **d**   **e**

Exercise 5.7B _____

1 Find each labelled angle.

a   **b**   **c**   **d**   **e**

2 Find each labelled angle.

a   **b**   **c** 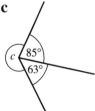   **d** 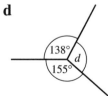   **e**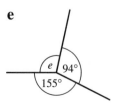

5.8 The angle sum of a triangle

The sum of the angles in any triangle is 180°.

Example

Find the angle marked x in triangle RST.

The three angles must total 180°.

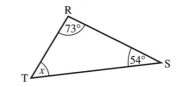

So: $x + 73 + 54 = 180$
$x + 127 = 180$
$x = 180 - 127 = 53$

So, $x = 53°$.

Exercise 5.8A

1 Find the angle marked x in each triangle.

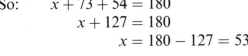

2 Two of the angles in a triangle are 33° and 51°.
Calculate the size of the third angle.

Exercise 5.8B

1 Calculate the angles marked ? in these triangles.

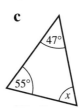

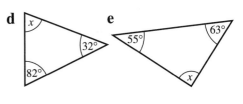

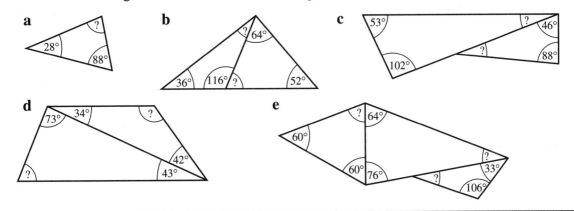

5.9 Types of triangle

All triangles have three straight edges and an angle sum of 180°.
Here are some special triangles:

- **Equilateral triangle**   has 3 edges the same length
                              3 equal angles – all 60°.

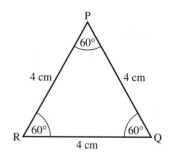

- **Isosceles triangle**   has 2 edges the same length
                            2 angles equal in size.

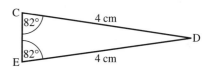

- **Acute-angled triangle**   has no angle greater than 90°.

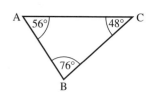

- **Obtuse-angled triangle**   has one angle greater than 90°.

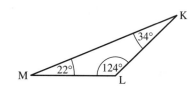

- **Right-angled triangle**   one angle is 90°.

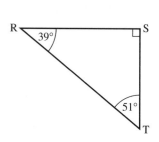

- **Scalene triangle**   has edges of different lengths
                          and angles different in size.

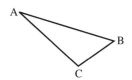

Exercise 5.9A _____

1 Look at these triangles.

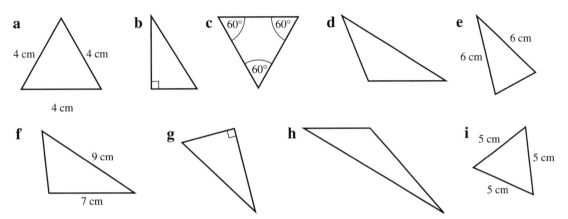

Copy and complete this table.

Triangle	Right-angled	Isosceles	Equilateral	Scalene
a			✓	
b				
c				
d				
e				
f				
g				
h				
i				

2 A triangle has angles of 58° and 66°.

  a Find the size of the other angle.

  b Is this triangle an acute-angled triangle?
    Explain your answer.

3 Triangle THF has angles of 38° and 44°.

  a Find the size of the other angle.

  b Is THF an obtuse-angled triangle? Explain your answer.

4 ABC is a right-angled isosceles triangle.

  a Which sides are equal in length?

  b Which angle is a right angle?

  c Find each angle of triangle ABC.

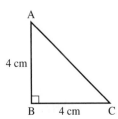

Exercise 5.9B

1 Look at these triangles.

a □ ⊿   b △   c ◺   d (8 cm / 8 cm, 8 cm base) △   e ◁   f (7 cm \ / 7 cm) ▽   g ◿

(58°) (58°)

Copy and complete this table.

Triangle	Equilateral	Acute-angled	Obtuse-angled	Isosceles	Right-angled
a					
b					
c					
d					
e					
f					
g					

2 Triangle ARN is equilateral.
The length of AR is 6.2 cm.

a What is the length of AN?
b What is the length of RN?
c Find the size of each angle.

3 In triangle ABC the angle at C is 41°.

a What is the size of angle B?
b Find angle A.

4 What is special about an obtuse-angled triangle?

5 a What is special about a right-angled triangle?
b Can a right-angled triangle have two angles that
are 90°? Give one reason for your answer.

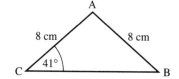

5.10 Constructing triangles

To construct shapes you must measure lines and angles
accurately.
Lines may be measured in centimetres or millimetres.
Angles are measured in degrees.

Example 1

Construct a right-angled triangle with a base of 4 cm and a height of 3 cm.
Find the length of the third side of the triangle.

- Draw the base line 4 cm long.

4 cm

- At one end of the base draw an angle of 90°.
  This is the height line of the triangle.

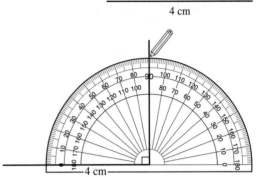

- Measure 3 cm along the height line.

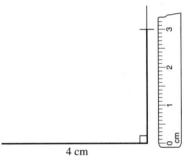

- Draw in and measure the third side of the triangle.

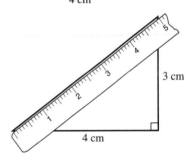

The third side is 5 cm long.

Exercise 5.10A

1 Copy this table, construct each right-angled triangle and complete the table.

Triangle	Base (cm)	Height (cm)	Third side (cm)
A	5	5	☐
B	6	4	☐
C	5	6	☐
D	4	7	☐

Exercise 5.10B

1 Copy this table, construct each right-angled triangle and
   complete the table.

Triangle	Base (cm)	Height (mm)	Third side (mm)
A	4	45	☐
B	5	55	☐
C	6	65	☐
D	4	75	☐
E	3	52	☐
F	4	38	☐
G	5	66	☐
H	7	32	☐
I	6	48	☐
J	8	25	☐

Example 2

The diagram shows a sketch of triangle ABC.

a Construct triangle ABC.
b Find the length of AB and
   the size of angle A.

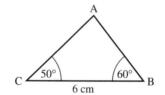

'Construct' is another
way of saying 'make an
accurate drawing'.

• Draw and label the base line CB, 6 cm long.

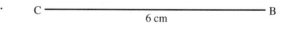

• At C draw an angle of 50°.

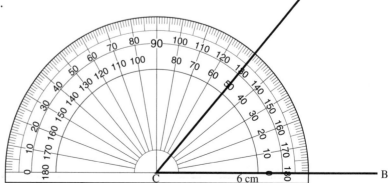

- At B draw an angle of 60°.

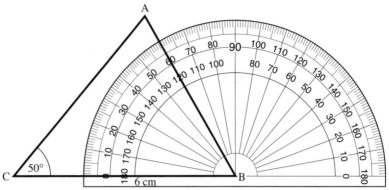

- Where the two lines at angles to the base cross is the point A.

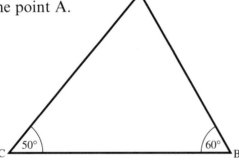

AB is 4.9 cm long.
The angle at A is 70°.

> You can check your drawing as the angle sum of a triangle is 180°. Here the third angle must be 70°.

Exercise 5.10C

1 The diagram shows a sketch of triangle KLM.
  a Construct triangle KLM.
  b Find the length of KL.
  c Find the size of the angle at K.

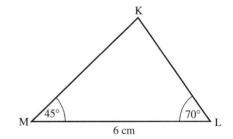

2 The diagram shows a sketch of triangle STV.
  a Construct triangle STV.
  b Find the length of SV.
  c Find the size of the angle at S.

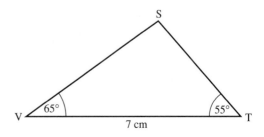

3 The diagram shows a
  sketch of triangle FGH.

  a Construct triangle FGH.
  b Find the length of the
     sides FG and FH.
  c Find the size of the angle at F.

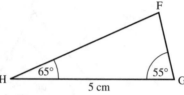

Check your triangle by
making sure it has an
angle sum of 180°.

4 The diagram shows a
  sketch of triangle BCD.

  a Construct triangle BCD.
  b Find the length of
     the sides BC and BD.
  c Find the size of the
     angle at B.

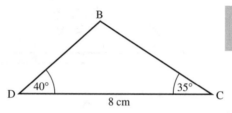

Check each triangle you
draw.

5 The diagram shows a sketch of triangle EFG.

  a Construct triangle EFG.
  b Find the length of the sides EF and EG.
  c Find the size of the angle at E.

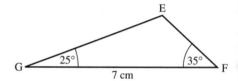

Exercise 5.10D

1 The diagram shows a sketch of triangle ABC.

  a Construct triangle ABC.
  b Find the length of the sides AB and AC.
  c Find the size of the angle at A.

2 The diagram shows a sketch of triangle JKL.

  a Construct triangle JKL.
  b Find the length of the sides JK and JL.
  c Find the size of the angle at J.

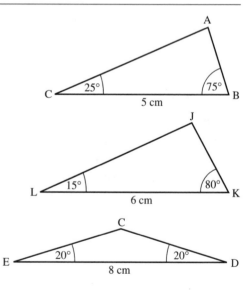

3 The diagram shows a sketch of triangle CDE.

  a Construct triangle CDE.
  b Find the length of the sides CD and CE.
  c Find the size of the angle at C.

4 The diagram shows a sketch of triangle LMN.

  a Construct triangle LMN.
  b Find the length of the sides LM and LN.
  c Find the size of the angle at L.

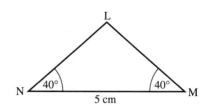

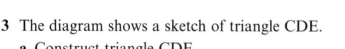

5 The diagram shows a sketch of triangle RST.

   a Construct triangle RST.
   b Find the length of the sides RS and RT.
   c Find the size of the angle at R.

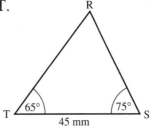

Using compasses

Example 3

Triangle ABC has sides of 7 cm, 4 cm and 5 cm.
Construct triangle ABC.

- Choose one side for the base and draw
  this accurately.

7 cm

- With a pair of compasses open
  to 4 cm, put the point at one end
  of the base and draw an arc.

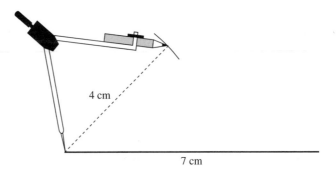

- Open the compasses to 5 cm and with the point at the
  other end of the base draw a second arc.

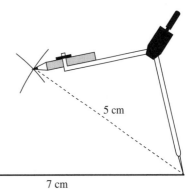

- Join each end of the base to the point
  where the arcs cross.
  Label your triangle.

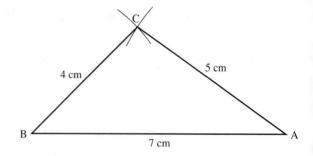

Exercise 5.10E

1 a Copy this table.
  b Construct each triangle.
  c Measure all three angles in the triangle.
  d Complete the table.

Triangle	Sides (cm)			Angles (°)		
A	8	5	6			
B	3	4	5			
C	5	7	8			
D	4	5	6			
E	5	7	7			
F	8	5	5			
G	7	6	8			
H	6	6	6			
I	5	5	5			

Exercise 5.10F

1 a Copy this table.
  b Construct each triangle.
  c Measure all three angles in the triangle.
  d Complete the table.

Triangle	Sides (cm)			Angles (°)		
A	6	5	6			
B	5	4	7			
C	6	7	4			
D	8	7	8			
E	6	4	5			
F	4	4	4			
G	7.5	6	8			
H	6	6.5	6			
I	5	5.5	5.5			

5.11 Line symmetry

▶ A shape has a **line of symmetry** if one side of a shape is
a reflection of the other.
A shape can have more than one line of symmetry.

You can use a mirror to help you decide if a shape has
line symmetry.

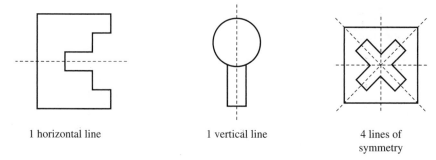

| 1 horizontal line | 1 vertical line | 4 lines of symmetry |

These shapes have **line symmetry**.

Exercise 5.11A

1 Here are the letters of the alphabet:

A B C D E F G H I J K L M
N O P Q R S T U V W X Y Z

  a Which letters have a vertical line of symmetry?
  b Which ones have a horizontal line of symmetry?
  c Draw the letter **H**. Draw in all its lines of symmetry.

2 Look at the word **COD**.
  a Write **COD** and draw in a line of symmetry for the
    word.
  b Write **MUM** and draw in a line of symmetry for the
    word.

3 **a** Draw a square. Draw in all its lines of symmetry.
    How many lines of symmetry does it have?
  b Draw a rectangle.
    Draw in all its lines of symmetry.

4 a Decide if each of these European road signs has line symmetry.
   b If it has, copy it and draw in all its lines of symmetry.

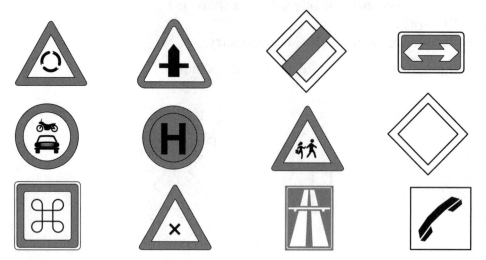

Exercise 5.11B _____

1 a Sketch these triangles.
   b Draw in all their lines of symmetry.

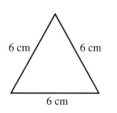   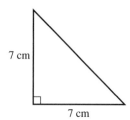   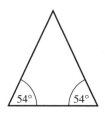 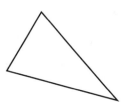

2 Here are some types of quadrilateral.

   a Copy and label each shape.
   b Draw in all the lines of symmetry.

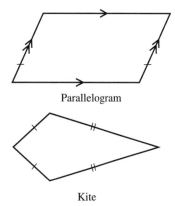

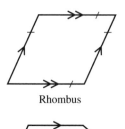

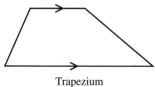

3 These designs are not complete.
Each dotted line is a line of symmetry.
Copy each one and draw the complete design.

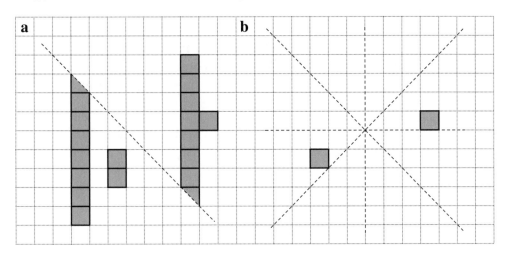

4 In a tile arrangement black and white square tiles must
join along a complete edge.

  a Draw all the different ways that 4 tiles can be arranged.
    (You can use from 0 to 4 tiles of either colour.)
  b On each arrangement draw in any lines of symmetry.

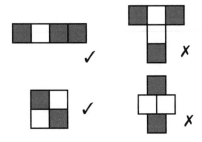

5.12 3-D shapes

A 3-D shape has length, width and height.

The simplest 3-D shape is a cube.

A cube has 8 vertices
          6 faces   [all the same size]
          12 edges   [all the same length]

> 3-D is short for
> three dimensional.

> The plural of vertex
> is 'vertices'.

- A cuboid

  6 faces   [not all the same size]
  8 vertices
  12 edges   [not all the same length]

- A prism

  This is a triangular prism.
  Wherever you cut along its length you
  will get the same shape triangle.

- A pyramid

  This is a pyramid with a square base.

- A cylinder

  A tin of beans is a cylinder shape.

- A sphere

  A snooker ball is a sphere.

3-D shapes often have **plane symmetry**.

A 3-D shape has plane symmetry if it can be cut into two
identical pieces so that each piece is a mirror image of the
other.

Note: Plane symmetry is
similar to line symmetry
for 2-D (flat) shapes.

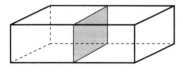

This cuboid can be cut down the middle
into two identical halves.

Can you see any other ways of cutting it
to give a mirror image?

Exercise 5.12A

1 How many faces does a triangular prism have?

2 Give an example of an everyday object that is a cuboid.

3 Give an example of an everyday object that is a cylinder.

4 Is a rugby ball a sphere?
Explain your answer.

5 Explain how a cube and a cuboid are different.

6 Describe one plane of symmetry of a cylinder.
Illustrate your answer by means of a diagram.

Exercise 5.12B _____

1 How many faces does a pyramid with a square base
have?

2 How many vertices has a pyramid with a square base?

3 Think of a pyramid with a base that is a triangle.
  a How many vertices does it have?
  b How many faces does it have?

4 Explain how a cuboid and a cylinder are different.

5 A cuboid is cut up to make 3 cubes where every edge
is 4 cm.
What are the length, width and height of the original
cuboid?
Draw a diagram to show what you mean.

6 Describe two planes of symmetry of a square-based
pyramid. Illustrate your answer using diagrams.

_____

Revision Exercise 5   *Review*

1 Give each of these turns in degrees.
  a $\frac{1}{4}$ of a full turn   **b** $\frac{2}{3}$ of a full turn   **c** $\frac{1}{5}$ of a full turn.   *Unit 5.1*

2 Give this clockwise turn in degrees.
Face N. Turn to face W.   *Unit 5.1*

3 Copy and complete this table for the radar display.

Letter	Location
A	
B	
C	
D	
E	
F	
G	
H	
I	
J	
K	

Unit 5.2

4 Mark a point A on your page.
Draw and label a North line at A.
Draw and label these bearings from A.

a 080°   **b** 110°   **c** 145°   **d** 225°   **e** 305°

Unit 5.3

5 From a point A a boat can be seen 400 metres away on a bearing of 165°.
A lighthouse is 600 metres away on a bearing of 235°.

a Use a scale of 1 cm = 100 metres and draw a diagram to show the point A, the boat, and the lighthouse.

b In a straight line, how far is the boat from the lighthouse?

Unit 5.3

6 For each angle say if it is obtuse, acute or reflex.

a 48°   **b** 165°   **c** 72°
d 315°   **e** 185°   **f** 135°

Unit 5.4

7 Estimate, then measure accurately the size of each angle.

a   **b**   **c**

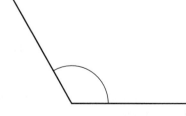

Unit 5.5

8 a Measure each interior angle
in this shape.
b Find the total of the four
interior angles.

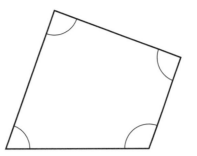

Unit 5.6

Review

9 Draw these angles accurately.
a 55°   **b** 80°
c 125°   **d** 155°   *Unit 5.6*

10 Calculate the labelled angle in each case.

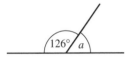 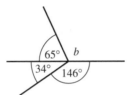 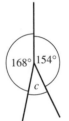

Unit 5.7

11 Find the angle marked *x* in each triangle.

a    **b**   **c**    **d**

Unit 5.8

12 a What is special about isosceles triangle?
b What can you say about an equilateral triangle?
c Give the size of each angle in:
an isosceles right-angled triangle.   *Unit 5.9*

13 a Construct a right angled triangle with a base of 6 cm
and a height of 8 cm.
b Find the length of the third side of the triangle.   *Unit 5.10*

14 The diagram shows a sketch of triangle ABC.

   a Construct triangle ABC.
   b Find the length of AB.
   c Find the size of the angle at A.

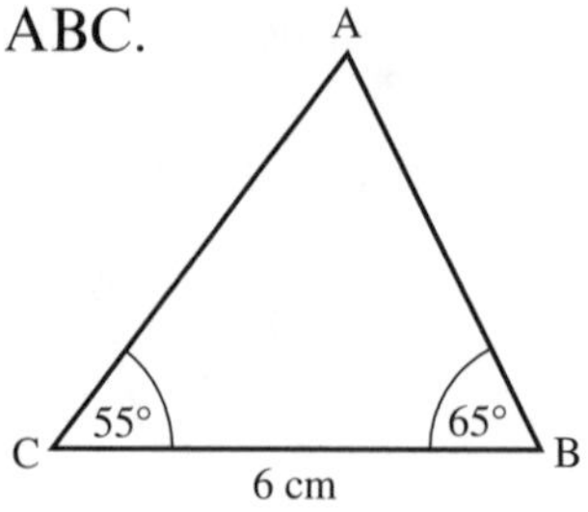

Review

A

C 55°　　　6 cm　　　65° B

Unit 5.10

15 a Construct a triangle with sides of 6 cm, 5 cm and 6 cm.
   b Give the size of each angle in the triangle.

16 Write the word **T A T**.
Draw in a line of symmetry for the word. *Unit 5.11*

17 Write a letter of the alphabet that has 2 lines of symmetry. Show them. *Unit 5.11*

18 Draw a square. Show all its lines of symmetry. *Unit 5.11*

19 Draw a kite. How many lines of symmetry has the shape? *Unit 5.11*

20 How many lines of symmetry has a circle? Explain your answer. *Unit 5.11*

21 a Sketch a triangular prism.
   b How many faces has a triangular prism?
   c How many vertices has it? *Unit 5.12*

22 Give an example of an everyday object that is a cylinder in shape. *Unit 5.12*

23 How many planes of symmetry has a square based pyramid?
Make a sketch to explain your answer. *Unit 5.12*

Investigation

Diagonal challenge

A rectangle has two diagonals, but what about other shapes? If you know how many edges a shape has do you know how many diagonals it has?

- try out some shapes.
- is there a pattern?
- can you predict the number of diagonals?

6 TRANSFORMATIONS

6.1 Reflection

▶ When you reflect an object in a mirror the image is the same distance from the mirror as the object.

▶ A line joining corresponding points on the object and the image cuts the mirror at 90°.

▶ To describe a reflection you describe the mirror line.

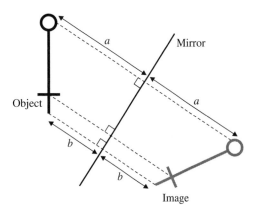

Exercise 6.1A _____

1 a Trace Shape A and its mirror line.
 b Reflect Shape A in the mirror and draw its image.

> **Hint:**
> Fold your tracing paper along the mirror line to find where the image will lie.

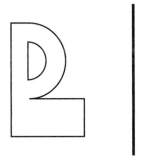

Shape A

2 Some capital letters look the same when reflected in a mirror. For example:

A looks the same in a vertical mirror   **A | A**

C looks the same in a horizontal mirror $\frac{C}{C}$

 a Which letters from the alphabet look the same in a vertical mirror?
 b Which letters look the same in a horizontal mirror?

3 a Draw the reflection of **N** in a vertical mirror.
  b Draw the reflection of **Z** in a horizontal mirror.

4 A number **4** is reflected in a mirror.
  a What things about the shape stay the same *after* the reflection?
  b What things change after the reflection?

Exercise 6.1B

1 Copy each shape and its mirror line.
  Reflect the shape and draw the image.

a

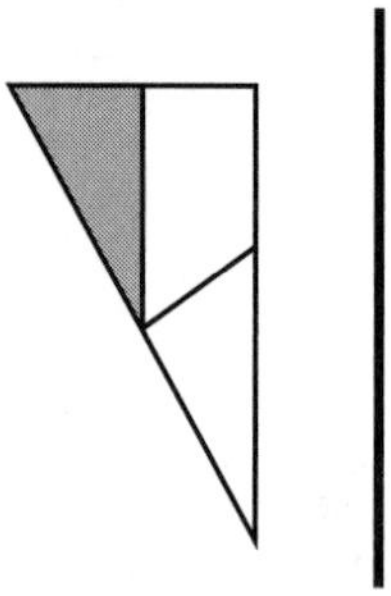

b

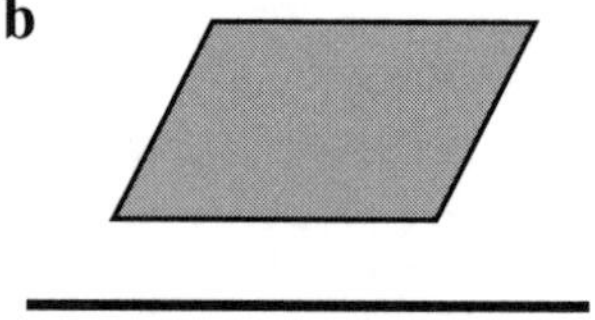

c

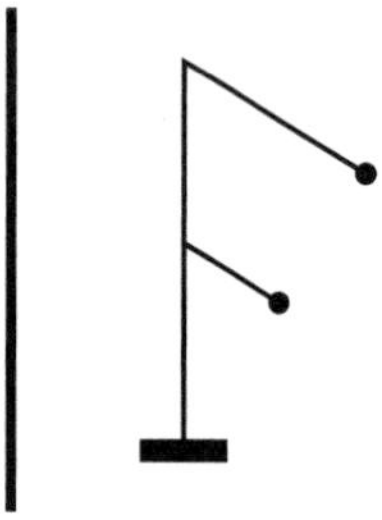

d

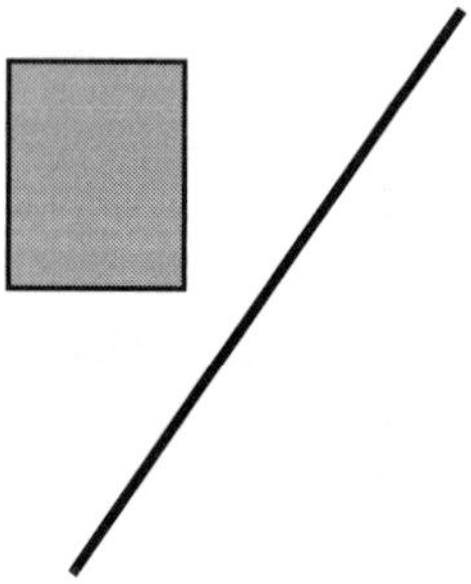

e

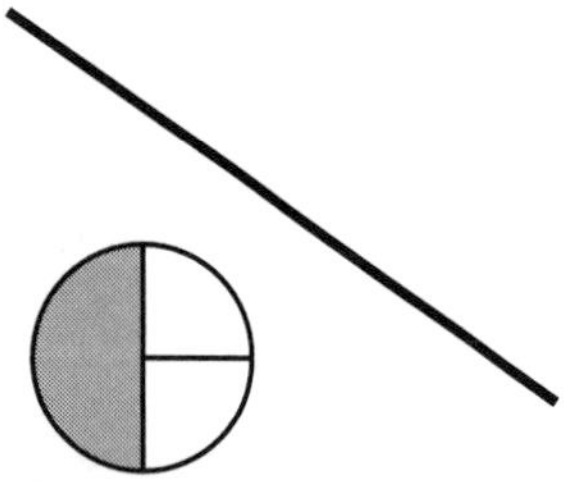

f

2 **a** Copy the axes and Shape A onto squared paper.

b Reflect A in the *x*-axis and draw the image B.

c Reflect B in the *x*-axis. What do you discover?

d Reflect A in the *y*-axis and draw the image C.

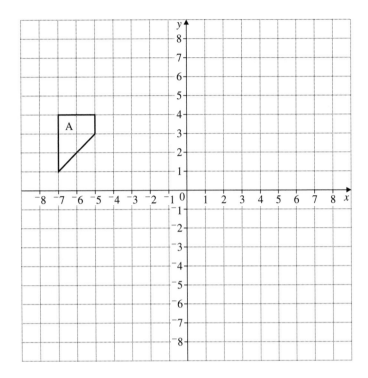

3 Copy this diagram. Draw the image of A after reflection in:

a Line 1

b Line 2

c Line 3

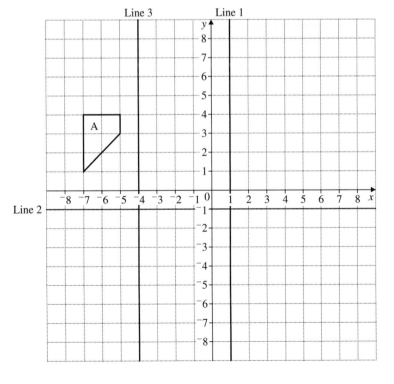

4 Copy this diagram.
Draw the image of A
after reflection in:

a Line 1

b Line 2

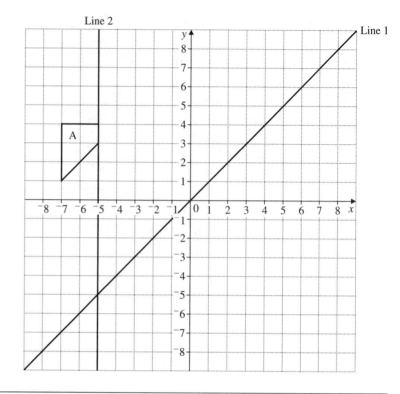

6.2 Rotation

To rotate a shape you turn it.

▶ To describe a rotation you must give
this information:

* The angle through which the object
  turns.
* The direction (clockwise or
  anticlockwise).
* The centre of rotation (sometimes
  given by a pair of coordinates).

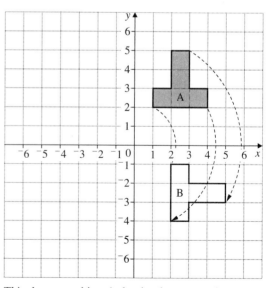

This shows an object A that has been rotated
90° clockwise about **the point (0, 0)** to give image B.

Exercise 6.2A _____

1 a Copy the grid on p. 130 and the object A.

b ● Place tracing paper over the diagram.
  ● Trace the object **and the axes**.
  ● Put your pencil point on (0, 0).
  ● Turn the tracing paper 90° anticlockwise about your
    pencil point.
  ● Draw the image and label it C.

c Describe the rotation from A to C.

2 On another copy of object A and the axes:

a Rotate A 180° clockwise about the point (0, 0).
  Draw and label the image D.

b Rotate D 180° clockwise about the point (0, 0).
  What do you discover about its position?

> **Hint:**
> By tracing the axes as
> well you can easily see
> when the paper has made
> a turn of 90°, 180° or
> 270°.

3 On another copy of object A and the axes:

a Rotate A 270° clockwise about the point (0, 0).
  Draw and label this image as E.

b Compare images C and E.
  Explain why this happens.

4 Describe a rotation that will take object P onto:

a image Q

b image R

c image S

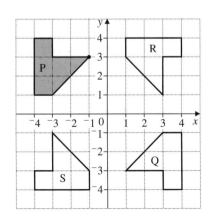

Exercise 6.2B

1 This question uses other points for the centre of rotation.
   Copy this grid and object A.

   a Rotate A 180° about the
      point (3, 3).
      Label this image B.

   b Rotate A 90° anticlockwise
      about the point (0, 1).
      Label this image C.

   c Rotate A 90° anticlockwise
      about the point (3, ⁻1).
      Label this image D.

   d Rotate A 90° clockwise about
      the point (1, 2).
      Label this image E.

   e Describe two different
      rotations that will take E
      back to D.

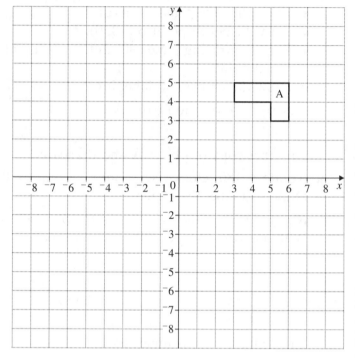

2 This object A is rotated 90°
   anticlockwise about the
   point (1, 1).

   a Copy the diagram show the
      shape after this rotation.

   b Give a clockwise rotation
      that will take it back to
      its original position.

   c Give an anticlockwise
      rotation that will take it
      back to its original position.

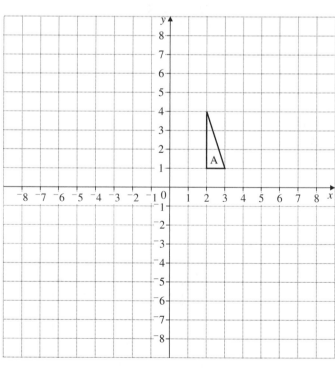

3 Copy and complete this table.

A rotation of	does the same as	a rotation of
90° clockwise	does the same as	☐ anticlockwise
180° anticlockwise	does the same as	☐ clockwise
90° anticlockwise	does the same as	☐ clockwise
60° clockwise	does the same as	☐ anticlockwise
80° anticlockwise	does the same as	☐ clockwise

6.3 Translation

▶ A translation is a sliding movement without turns.
You describe a translation using a vector like this:

$\binom{3}{2}$ — move 3 units parallel to the x-axis then
— move 2 units parallel to the y-axis.

Note:
A negative move right is a move left.
A negative move up is a move down.

Example

Show Triangle A after a translation of $\binom{4}{-2}$.

Each vertex of the triangle moves:

4 units to the right along x-axis: 2 units down along the y-axis:

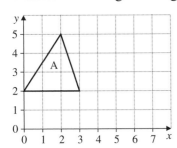   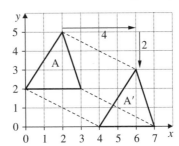

Exercise 6.3A _____

1 Copy and complete these statements. The first one is done for you.

  a The vector $\binom{-4}{7}$ means move ..4.. spaces ..left.. and ..7.. spaces ..up..

b The vector $\begin{pmatrix} 2 \\ 3 \end{pmatrix}$ means move .... spaces .... and .... spaces .....

c The vector $\begin{pmatrix} 3 \\ 0 \end{pmatrix}$ means move .... spaces .... and .... spaces .....

d The vector $\begin{pmatrix} ^-2 \\ ^-5 \end{pmatrix}$ means move .... spaces .... and .... spaces .....

2 Copy this diagram.

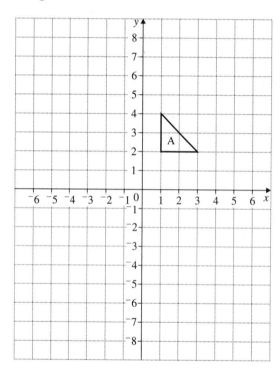

Translate the triangle A by each vector and label each image.

a $\begin{pmatrix} 2 \\ 3 \end{pmatrix}$; label B

b $\begin{pmatrix} ^-4 \\ 2 \end{pmatrix}$; label C

c $\begin{pmatrix} ^-6 \\ ^-4 \end{pmatrix}$; label D

d $\begin{pmatrix} 2 \\ ^-5 \end{pmatrix}$; label E

e $\begin{pmatrix} 4 \\ 0 \end{pmatrix}$; label F

f $\begin{pmatrix} 0 \\ ^-6 \end{pmatrix}$; label G

Exercise 6.3B _____

1 Copy this diagram.
Translate the spot A by each vector and
show its final position.

a $\begin{pmatrix} ^-6 \\ 0 \end{pmatrix}$ b $\begin{pmatrix} ^-2 \\ 3 \end{pmatrix}$

c $\begin{pmatrix} 2 \\ 5 \end{pmatrix}$ d $\begin{pmatrix} ^-5 \\ ^-2 \end{pmatrix}$

e $\begin{pmatrix} ^-4 \\ 8 \end{pmatrix}$ f $\begin{pmatrix} 0 \\ 9 \end{pmatrix}$

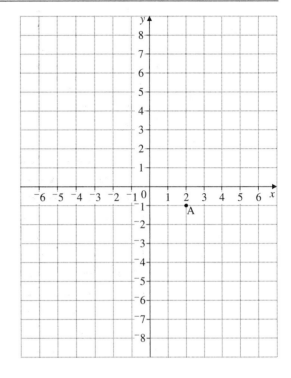

2 Copy the grid and the T shape.

a Translate the T by the vector $\begin{pmatrix} ^-1 \\ 3 \end{pmatrix}$.

b Translate this image by $\begin{pmatrix} ^-5 \\ 0 \end{pmatrix}$.

c Translate this image by $\begin{pmatrix} ^-2 \\ ^-5 \end{pmatrix}$.

d Translate this image by $\begin{pmatrix} 4 \\ ^-4 \end{pmatrix}$.

e Translate this image by $\begin{pmatrix} 4 \\ 6 \end{pmatrix}$.

f What do you discover?

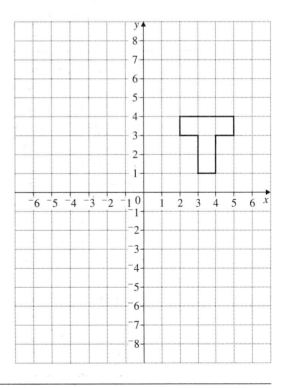

Revision Exercise 6

1 Copy each shape and its mirror line. Reflect the shape and draw the image.

a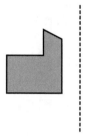

b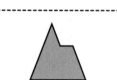

c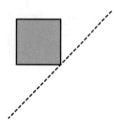

Unit 6.1

2 a Copy the axes and Shape A onto squared paper.
  b Reflect A in the *x*-axis and draw the image. Label it B.
  c Reflect A in the *y*-axis and draw the image. Label it C.

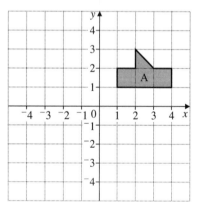

Unit 6.1

3 a Copy the grid and the object A.
  b Rotate A by 90° clockwise about (0, 0). Label the image B.
  c Rotate A by 180° about (0, 0). Label the image C.

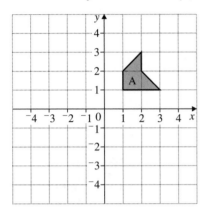

Unit 6.2

4 a Copy the grid and the object A.

  b Translate A by the vector $\begin{pmatrix} -3 \\ 1 \end{pmatrix}$. Label the image B.

  b Translate A by the vector $\begin{pmatrix} 2 \\ -2 \end{pmatrix}$. Label the image C.

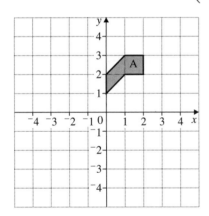

Unit 6.2

5 What vector describes a move of 5 to the right along the
  x-axis and 4 down along the y-axis?   *Unit 6.3*

7 MEASURES

7.1 Reading scales and dials

You read a scale on a measuring device which might be a
ruler, a gauge or a dial.
Some scales are more accurate than others and sometimes
you must estimate.

Example 1

What value is shown by each of the arrows:

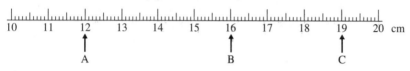

> When you read a scale
> you must decide what
> each mark on the scale
> stands for.

    Arrow A shows 12 cm.
    Arrow B shows 16 cm.
    Arrow C shows 19 cm.

Example 2

What value is shown by each arrow?

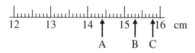

> Decide how you will
> write the value you read
> from the scale.

    Arrow A shows 14.4 cm.
    Arrow B shows 15.3 cm.
    Arrow C shows 15.8 cm.

Exercise 7.1A

1 Give the value shown by each arrow on the scale.

  a
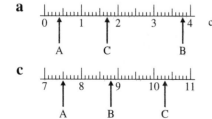

  b
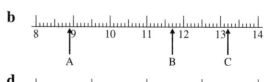

  c

  d
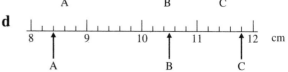

2 Estimate the values shown by each arrow on the
scale.

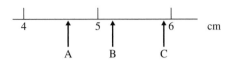

Exercise 7.1B _____

1 Give the value shown by each arrow on the scale.

a

2 Estimate the values shown by each arrow on the scale.

Exercise 7.1C _____

1 Copy this scale.

Put these arrows on the scale.

     Arrow A at 16.   Arrow B at 21.
     Arrow C at 23.   Arrow D at 19.

2 Copy this scale.

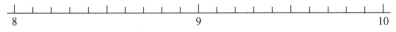

Put these arrows on the scale.

     Arrow A at 8.4   Arrow B at 9.3
     Arrow C at 8.7   Arrow D at 9.9

3 Copy this scale.

0   50 Litres

Put in arrows to show your estimate.

    Arrow A at 30 litres.   Arrow B at 45 litres.
    Arrow C at 12 litres.   Arrow D at 18 litres.

4 Estimate the value shown by each arrow.

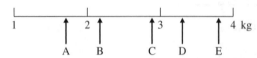

Exercise 7.1D

1 Estimate the value shown by the arrows on the scale in each diagram.

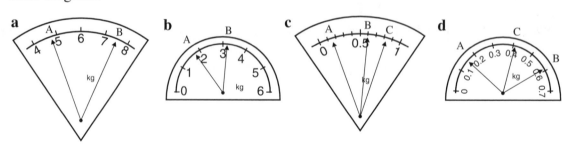

2 Give the value shown by each arrow on this scale.

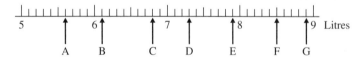

3 Draw a scale from 3 to 5.
On your scale place these arrows.
You need to estimate the values.

    Arrow A at 3.1   Arrow B at 3.5
    Arrow C at 3.9   Arrow D at 4.2
    Arrow E at 4.6   Arrow F at 4.95

Some scales are more accurate than others.
This scale shows values between 4.5 and 4.6

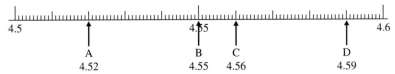

Exercise 7.1E

1 What value is shown by each arrow?

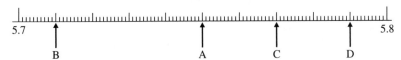

2 What value is shown by each arrow?

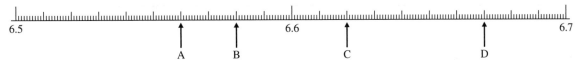

3 What value is shown by each arrow?

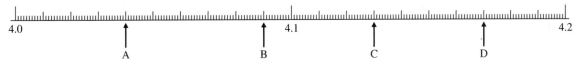

Exercise 7.1F

1 What value is shown by each arrow?

2 What value is shown by each arrow?

3 What value is shown by each arrow?

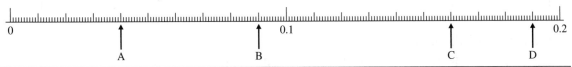

7.2 Metric and Imperial measure

To measure length you can use metric or imperial units. The centimetre (cm) is a metric unit and the inch (in) is an imperial unit.

You may need to convert between units so it is useful to know that 1 inch $= 2.54$ cm.

This table shows the conversions you need to know.

	Metric	Imperial	Some approximate conversions
Length	10 mm = 1 cm 100 cm = 1 m 1000 m = 1 km	12 inches = 1 foot 3 feet = 1 yard 1760 yards = 1 mile	1 inch is about 2.5 cm 1 foot is about 30.5 cm 1 metre is about 39.4 in 1 mile is about 1.61 km

Exercise 7.2A

1 Give each of these lengths in millimetres (mm).

    a 12 cm   **b** 3 cm   **c** 3.5 cm   **d** 17.6 cm   **e** 19.2 cm   **f** 26.3 cm

    g 1 metre   **h** 1.5 m   **i** 10 m   **j** 4.6 m   **k** 3.15 m   **l** 0.8 m

2 Give each of these lengths in centimetres (cm).

    a 5 m   **b** 1.2 m   **c** 3.3 m   **d** 1.8 m   **e** 6.4 m   **f** 12.6 m

    g 40.7 m   **h** 355 m   **i** 566.5 m   **j** 0.7 m   **k** 1.38 m   **l** 0.07 m

Exercise 7.2B

1 Give each of these lengths in centimetres (cm).

    a 2 in   **b** 5 in   **c** 10 in   **d** 3.5 in   **e** 2 ft   **f** 7.8 ft

2 Give each of these lengths in inches (in).

    a 1 cm   **b** 4 cm   **c** 9.5 cm   **d** 2 m   **e** 8 m   **f** 1.26 m

3 Give each of these lengths in kilometres (km).

    a 3 miles   **b** 10 miles   **c** 175 miles   **d** 2.81 miles   **e** $5\frac{1}{4}$ miles   **f** $7\frac{3}{4}$ miles

4 Give each of these lengths in miles.

    a 1 km   **b** 16 km   **c** 3.26 km   **d** 181 m   **e** $4\frac{1}{2}$ km   **f** $6\frac{1}{4}$ km

For mass you can also use metric or imperial units.

	Metric	Imperial	Some approximate conversions
Mass	1000 g = 1 kg 1000 kg = 1 tonne	16 oz = 1 lb 14 lb = 1 stone 2240 lbs = 1 ton	1 pound (lb) is about 454 g 1 kg is about 2.21 lb

Exercise 7.2C

1 Give each of these weights in grams (g).

   a 3 kg   **b** 10 kg   **c** 25 kg   **d** 1.5 kg   **e** 0.5 kg   **f** 0.25 kg

   g 5.25 kg   **h** 7.6 kg   **i** 7.06 kg   **j** 0.1 kg   **k** 0.01 kg   **l** 0.001 kg

2 Give each of these weights in kilograms (kg).

   a 3 tonnes   **b** 12 tonnes   **c** 10 tonnes   **d** 45 tonnes

   e 0.5 tonnes   **f** 4.5 tonnes   **g** 1.4 tonnes   **h** 8.6 tonnes

   i 7.3 tonnes   **j** 0.8 tonnes   **k** 0.08 tonnes   **l** 0.008 tonnes

3 Give each of these weights in ounces (oz).

   a 4 lb   **b** 5 lb   **c** 25 lb   **d** $\frac{1}{2}$ lb   **e** $\frac{1}{4}$ lb   **f** $\frac{3}{4}$ lb

   g $2\frac{1}{2}$ lb   **h** $5\frac{1}{4}$ lb   **i** $7\frac{3}{4}$ lb   **j** $12\frac{1}{2}$ lb **k** $7\frac{1}{4}$ lb   **l** $5\frac{3}{4}$ lb

Exercise 7.2D

1 Convert each of these weights to pounds (lb).

   a 2 kg   **b** 5 kg   **c** 2.34 kg

2 Convert each of these weights to grams (g).

   a 3 lb   **b** 7.5 lb   **c** $3\frac{1}{4}$ lb

3 Convert each of these weights to kilograms (kg)

   a 1 lb   **b** 6 lb   **c** $7\frac{3}{4}$ lb

Similarly for capacity you can use metric or imperial units.

	Metric	Imperial	Some approximate conversions
Capacity	10 ml = 1 cl 100 cl = 1 litre also 1000 ml = 1 litre	8 pints = 1 gallon	1 gallon is about 4.55 litres 1 litre is about 1.76 pints 1 litre is about 0.22 gallons

Exercise 7.2E

1 Convert each of these to millilitres (ml).
   a 3 litres   b $\frac{1}{2}$ litre
   c 14 litres   d 250 litres

2 Copy and complete: 60 ml = ☐ cl

3 How many cl in 15 litres?

4 How many pints in 14 gallons?

5 Convert 120 pints to gallons.

6 Copy and complete:
   Five gallons is about the same as ☐ litres.

Exercise 7.2F

1 Convert each of these to pints.
   a 2 litres (2 *l*)   b 5 litres   c 6.5 litres

2 Convert each of these to litres (*l*)
   a 3 gallons   b 6 gallons   c $3\frac{1}{4}$ gallons

3 a Which is larger: a 4 pint container of milk or a 2 litre
     container of milk?
   b Write down the difference between these two amounts
     in litres.

7.3 Solving conversion problems

Example

A watering can holds 3 Imperial gallons.
Roughly how many litres will this watering can hold?

From the table of units:
   1 gallon is about 4.55 gallons

   The watering can holds 3 gallons
       which is about 3 × 4.55 litres
       which is 13.65 litres.

The watering can will hold about 13.65 litres.

Exercise 7.3A _____

1 A dairy produces 14 240 pint bottles of milk in a shift.
How many gallons is this?

2 A case holds 12 bottles. Each bottle holds 75 cl.
How many litres of wine in a case?

3 A jam making plant uses 420 lb of sugar an hour.
Roughly how many kilograms is this?

4 The distance from John O'Groats to Lands End is
868 miles.
Roughly how many kilometres is this?

5 A trench is 16 inches wide.
Give this width in cm.

6 A sack of potatoes weighs 52 lb.
Roughly how many kilograms is this?

7 35 litres of olive oil is put into pint bottles.
a How many pint bottles can be filled with oil?
b How much oil is left over?

8 On West Street the lamps are 14 yards apart.
a How many feet apart are the lamps?
b Roughly how many metres apart are the lamps?

9 A tank holds 1250 litres of oil.
a Roughly how many gallons is this?
The tank holds fuel for a boiler.
The boiler uses 85 cl of oil each hour.
b For how many hours will a full tank of oil last?

10 A coffee shop uses 35 lb of sugar in a week.
a Roughly how many kilograms of sugar is this?
The shop is open six days a week.
b Roughly how many grams of sugar a day is this?

Exercise 7.3B _____

1 The length of a carpet is 23 feet.
a Roughly what this is in cm?
b Roughly how long is the carpet in metres?

2 Two towns are 4 miles apart.

   a How many yards is this?

   b How many feet is this?

3 An aircraft has 3850 litres of fuel.

   a Roughly how many gallons is this?

   b Jim says this is about 2200 pints of fuel.
      Is this a good estimate? Explain your answer.

4 A man weighs 168 lb.
   What is his weight in kilograms?

5 A 50 metre length of pipe is cut into these lengths:

       3 pieces   2.6 m long
       4 pieces   6 feet long
       5 pieces   88 cm long
       2 pieces   4 yards long

Roughly how much pipe is left over?
Show all your working.

6 A fitness course is 1540 yd long.
   People say it is about one and a half kilometres long.
   Is this a good estimate?
   Explain your answer by showing all your calculations.

7 A truck carries 30 tonnes of stone.

   a How many kilograms is this?

   The stone is then packed into bags.
   A bag of stone weighs 50 lb.

   b How many bags can be filled from a truck load of
      stone?

   c Roughly how much stone will be left over?

8 Cara sells orange juice by the glass.
   Each glass holds 250 ml.
   Cara buys juice in cartons that hold 5 litres.

   a How many glasses can she fill from one carton?

   b Roughly how many pints of juice are in a carton?

9 A gymnast weighs eight and a half stone.

   a Give the weight in lb.

   b Roughly what does the gymnast weigh in kg?

10 A tractor with a loaded trailer need to cross the bridge.
The tractor weighs 3 tonnes.
The trailer weighs 1460 kg.
The load weighs 2550 lb.
The driver weighs 12 stones.
Can the tractor and loaded trailer safely cross the bridge?
Explain your answer.

7.4 Reading graphs

One type of graph is a conversion graph.
When you read a graph like this you may have to estimate.

Example 1

Use this conversion graph to complete this table.

Ounces	Grams
5	140
8	225
1.5	☐
☐	170

From the graph:

    1.5 ounces converts to 42 grams
    170 grams converts to 6 ounces.

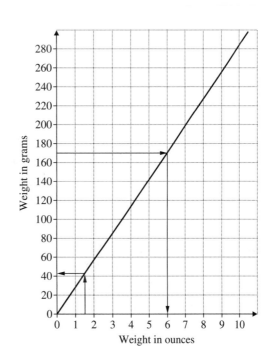

Exercise 7.4A

1 Copy and complete this table.

Estimated conversions	Ounces	Grams
A	7	☐
B	☐	118
C	3	☐
D	☐	240
E	1	☐

2 A mole was found in a garden.
   Its weight was found to be 6 ounces.
   What is the weight of the mole in grams?

3 A bag was found to hold 250 grams of sweets.
   Roughly how many ounces is this?

4 The weights of three small frogs were 80 g, 100 g and 30 g.
   Find the total weight of the frogs in ounces.

5 A parcel was weighed for posting. It weighed 350 grams.
   What did the parcel weigh in ounces?

Exercise 7.4B

1 Copy and complete this table.

Estimated conversions	Ounces	Grams
A	2	☐
B	☐	190
C	4.5	☐
D	☐	150
E	8.5	☐

2 A young rabbit was found at the side of a road.
   Its weight was found to be 270 grams.
   What is the weight of the rabbit in ounces?

3 A bag was found to hold five and a half ounces of sweets.
   Roughly how many grams is this?

4 The weights of two small mice were 3 ounces and $3\frac{1}{2}$ ounces.
Find the total weight of the mice in grams.

5 A parcel was weighed for posting. It weighed 14 ounces.
What did the parcel weigh in grams?

Example 2

The graph shows the temperature in a bakery
between 2 pm and 7 pm.

Estimate the temperature in the bakery at 4.30 pm.

The temperature at 4.30 pm was approximately
19.5 °C.

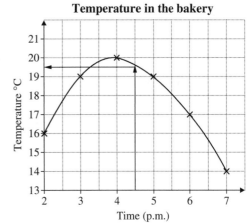

Exercise 7.4C

1 What was the temperature in the bakery at 6 pm?

2 a What was the highest temperature shown by the graph?
b At what time was this temperature reached?

3 Roughly at what time was the temperature 15 °C?

4 The temperature of 19 °C was recorded twice.
At what times was the temperature in the bakery 19 °C?

5 Dave said the temperature at a quarter to three was 19 °C.

a Do you agree with Dave?
b If you disagree, give your reason.

Exercise 7.4D

1 What was the temperature in the bakery at 2 pm?

2 a What was the lowest temperature shown by the graph?
b At what time was this temperature reached?

3 Roughly at what time was the temperature 14.5 °C?

4 The temperature of 18 °C was recorded twice.
At what times was the temperature in the bakery 18 °C?

5 By how many degrees did the temperature fall between 5 pm and 7 pm?

6 Between 2.30 pm and 4 pm, by how many degrees did the temperature rise?

7 Tom left the bakery at 5.30 pm.
What was the temperature at that time?

8 Jade started work at 6.15 pm.
Estimate the temperature in the bakery at this time.

9 Fans start in the bakery when the temperature gets to 18.5 °C.
   a Estimate from the graph the time that the fan switched on.
   b Estimate the time that the fan switched off.

10 In which hour shown by the graph was the fall in temperature greatest?

Travel graphs

Example 3

This graph shows the journey of a bus.

From the graph, estimate how far the bus was from the bus station at 9.45 am.

The bus was roughly 9.2 km from the bus station at 9.45 am.

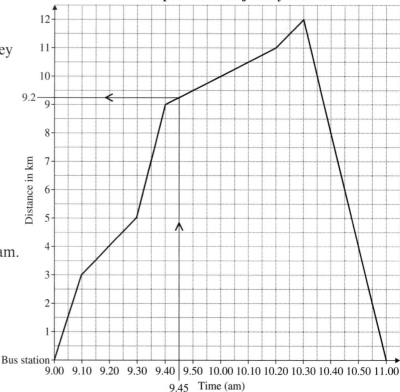

Graph to show the journey of a bus

Exercise 7.4E

1 At 10.20 am how far was the bus from the bus station?

2 Jim saw the bus at 9.30 am.
   At this time how far was the bus from the bus station?

3 How far did the bus travel between 9.10 am and 9.30 am?

4 At what time was the bus 12 km from the bus station?

5 The graph shows that the bus was 4 km from the bus
   station twice in its journey.
   At what times was the bus 4 km from the bus station?

6 In total, how far did the bus travel between 9 am and 11 am?

7 Estimate the times when the bus was 7 km from the bus station.

8 In the last 10 minutes of the journey how far did the bus travel?

9 Estimate how far the bus went in the first three quarters
   of an hour.

10 How long did the bus take to travel the last 13 km of its journey?

Exercise 7.4F

1 At 10.40 am how far was the bus from the bus station?

2 Jan saw the bus at 9.55 am.
   Estimate how far the bus was from the bus station?

3 Estimate how far the bus travelled between 9.25 am and 9.45 am?

4 Roughly at what times was the bus 10 km from the bus station?

5 The graph shows that the bus passed a post box 5 km from the
   bus station at 9.30 am.
   Estimate the time when the bus next passed this post box.

6 Estimate how far the bus travelled between 9.30 am and
   10.45 am?

7 Estimate how far the bus went in the first hour and a quarter.

8 Estimate when the bus was 8.5 km from the bus station.

9 Estimate how far the bus went in the first five minutes.

10 How long did the bus take to travel the first 20 km of its
   journey?

7.5 Time and the 24-hour clock

There are many units of time.
This table gives some of them.

Length of time	Is the same as
1 second	
1 minute	60 seconds
1 hour	60 minutes
1 day	24 hours
1 week	7 days
1 year	365 days
	366 in a leap-year
1 decade	10 years
1 century	100 years
1 millenium	1000 years

Exercise 7.5A

1 Copy and fill in this table.

Hours	Minutes	Seconds
1		
$\frac{1}{2}$		
$\frac{1}{4}$		
$\frac{3}{4}$		
$1\frac{1}{2}$		

2 Dave went on holiday for 5 weeks.
How many days was this?

3 Copy and complete:

   a 5 minutes = ☐ seconds

   b 540 seconds = ☐ minutes

   c 3 days = ☐ hours

   d 120 hours = ☐ days

   e 3 weeks = ☐ days

   f 56 days = ☐ weeks

   g 3 years = ☐ days, including a leap-year

4 It takes 4 seconds to print a poster.

   a How many posters can be printed in 1 hour?

   A shift is 8 hours long.

   b How many posters can be printed in one shift?

   Rina orders 420 posters of a new band.

   c How long will it take to print the posters?
     Give your answer in minutes.

5 Kim says he spends roughly two hours a day eating.
   Over 2 years, roughly how many days does Kim spend eating?

Exercise 7.5B

1 Copy and complete this table.

Days	Hours	Minutes
1	☐	☐
3	☐	☐
☐	120	☐
☐	288	☐
☐	☐	2880
☐	☐	7320

2 It takes a ship 8 weeks to sail from Hong Kong to Liverpool.
   How many days is this?

3 A trip to the Antarctic took 105 days.
   How many weeks is this?

4 A piece of pottery was said to have been made 4 centuries ago.
   How many years is this?

5 Jim has lived in the same hours for 3 decades.
   How many years is this?

6 A new car had a guarantee for 1000 days.

   a Roughly how many weeks is this?

   Liam says the guarantee is for more than 3 years.

   b Is Liam right?
     Explain your answer.

To write times of the day we may use **am** or **pm**.

- We use **am** for times between midnight and midday.
- We use **pm** for times between midday and midnight.

Example 1

Six o'clock in the morning is 6 am.
Six o'clock in the evening is 6 pm.

10 o'clock in the morning is 10 am.
10 o'clock at night is 10 pm.

Another word for midday is noon.

12 o'clock can be midday or midnight so we should write:

      12 midday
  or 12 midnight

Exercise 7.5C _____

1 Copy each of these sentences and write the time as **am** or **pm**.

    a Debbie gets up at 6 in the morning.
    b The train arrives at 11 tonight.
    c The film starts at 3 this afternoon.
    d School starts at 8.30.
    e Ian had lunch and got the bus to the match at 2 o'clock.

2 Give each answer as a time with **am** or **pm**.
   What time is:

    a three hours after 10 am
    b four hours before 3 pm
    c two hours after midnight
    d six hours before 1 pm
    e five hours after 10 pm?

3 A shop opens at 8 and closes at 9 each day.

    a Does the shop close at 9 am?
       Explain your answer.

   Mario says that the shop opens at 8 am.

    b Does this make sense? Explain.

Exercise 7.5D

1 Copy each sentence and write the time as **am** or **pm**.

   a The match was moved to the morning with kick-off at 11.

   b The lottery draw is at about 8 on each Saturday.

   c Ria works nights, she starts her shift at 10.

   d The plane landed this morning at 5.

   e Our post is never later than 7.30.

2 Give each answer as a time with **am** or **pm**.
What time is:

   a six hours before 2 pm

   b nine hours after 9 pm

   c one hour after 11.30 pm

   d three hours before 2 am

   e five hours before 3.30 am?

3 A group of fans left on the ferry at 10 pm on Friday.
The ferry was on time and got in at 3 am.
On what day did the ferry get in? Explain your answer.

Time may be given in the **24-hour clock system**.
These times start with 00.00 which is midnight.
24-hour clock times are used on bus and train timetables.
Times in the 24-hour clock system are written with 4 digits.

Example 2

2.30 am	is	02.30
9.20 am	is	09.20
10.15 am	is	10.15
1.25 pm	is	13.25
9.44 pm	is	21.44
11.35 pm	is	23.35

> To write pm times in the 24-hour clock system you add 12 to the hour numbers. 5.15 pm is 17.15

Exercise 7.5E

1 Write each of these times as a 24-hour time.

   a 5 am   **b** 9 am   **c** 2 pm   **d** 11.30 am

   e 5.20 pm   **f** 7.35 pm   **g** 10.45 pm   **h** 5.40 am

   i 11.10 pm   **j** 6.05 pm   **k** 11.25 am   **l** 2.55 am

2 Write each of these as a time with am or pm.

a 03.35	**b** 19.25	**c** 14.35	**d** 06.44
e 10.40	**f** 17.55	**g** 22.18	**h** 11.38
i 05.45	**j** 19.05	**k** 23.22	**l** 01.10

Exercise 7.5F

1   Write each of these times as a 24-hour clock time.

a 1.40 pm	**b** 10.35 pm	**c** 11.20 am	**d** 6.55 pm
e 7.15 am	**f** 1.05 am	**g** 11.10 pm	**h** 9.08 pm
i 3.50 pm	**j** 8.35 am	**k** 4.22 am	**l** 6.34 pm

2 Write each of these as a time with am or pm.

a 19.22	**b** 10.34	**c** 22.22	**d** 15.54
e 09.02	**f** 04.40	**g** 21.12	**h** 23.32
i 20.02	**j** 08.54	**k** 01.16	**l** 10.48

7.6 The perimeter of 2-D shapes

▶ The perimeter of a 2-D shape is the total distance around its outside edges.

The perimeter is given as a single length.

Example 1

Calculate the perimeter of this shape.

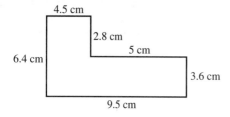

The shape has 6 edges.
The perimeter P is given by:

$$P = 6.4 + 4.5 + 2.8 + 5 + 3.6 + 9.5$$
$$= 31.8$$

The perimeter of the shape is 31.8 cm.

Exercise 7.6A

1 Calculate the perimeter of each of these shapes.

a
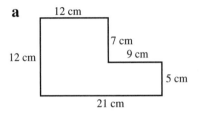

b
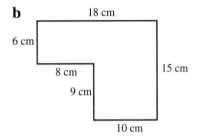

c
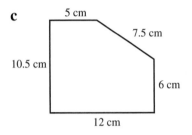

d
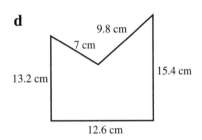

e
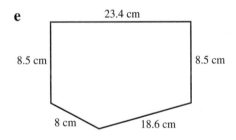

f
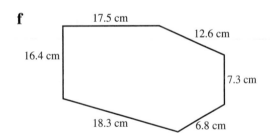

g
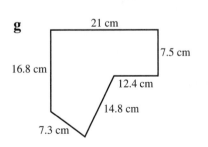

h
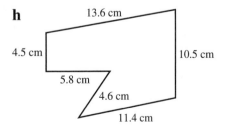

Exercise 7.6B

1 Find the perimeter of each of these shapes.

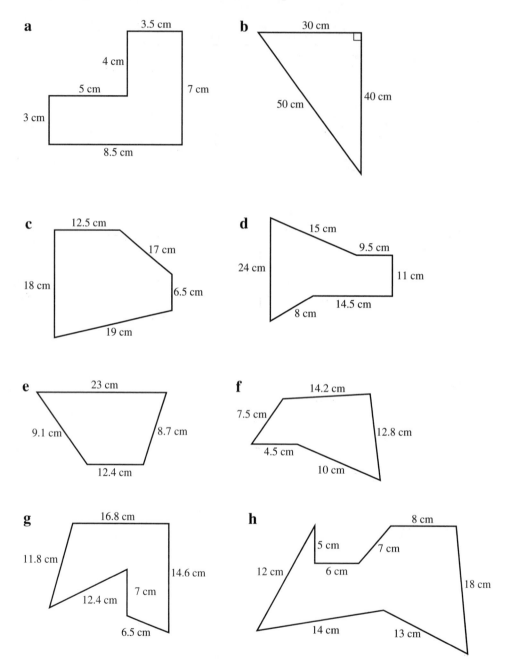

a

3.5 cm

4 cm

5 cm   7 cm

3 cm

8.5 cm

b

30 cm

50 cm   40 cm

c

12.5 cm

17 cm

18 cm   6.5 cm

19 cm

d

15 cm

9.5 cm

24 cm   11 cm

8 cm   14.5 cm

e

23 cm

9.1 cm   8.7 cm

12.4 cm

f

14.2 cm

7.5 cm

12.8 cm

4.5 cm

10 cm

g

16.8 cm

11.8 cm

14.6 cm

12.4 cm   7 cm

6.5 cm

h

8 cm

5 cm   7 cm

12 cm   6 cm

18 cm

14 cm   13 cm

You might have to calculate the length of one or more edges
so that you can calculate the perimeter.

Example 2

Calculate the perimeter of this shape.

The perimeter P is given by:

$$P = 9 + x + 5 + 7 + 4 + 12$$

We need the length of x.

From the diagram:

$$x + 7 = 12$$
$$x = 5$$

The perimeter P is given by:

$$P = 9 + 5 + 5 + 7 + 4 + 12$$
$$P = 42$$

The perimeter of the shape is 42 cm.

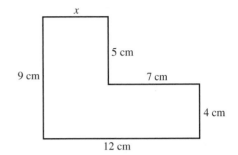

Exercise 7.6C _____

1 Find the missing sides, and the perimeter of each of these shapes.

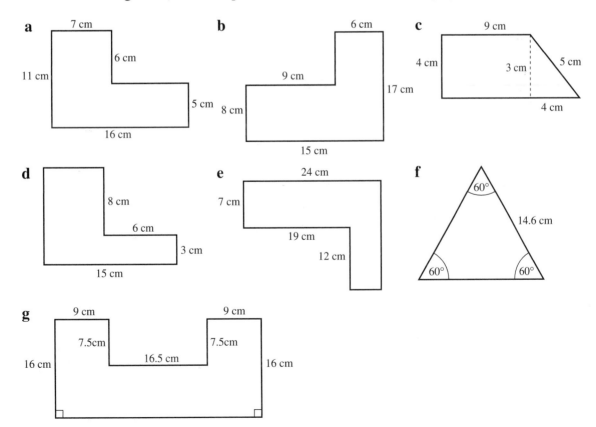

Exercise 7.6D _____

1 Find the missing sides, and the perimeter of each of these shapes.

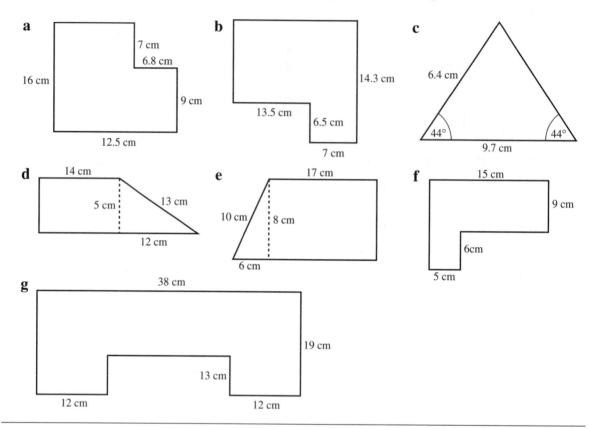

7.7 The area of 2-D shapes

The area of a 2-D shape is a measure of the amount of surface taken up by the shape. Area is measured in squared units, for example cm^2, m^2, km^2.

You can use a square grid to estimate the area of a shape.

Example 1

Find the area of this shape.

Counting squares the area is about $6\,cm^2$.

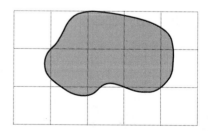

You may be able to count squares and find an exact area.

Example 2

Find the area of this shape.

Counting squares, the area of the shape is 12 cm².

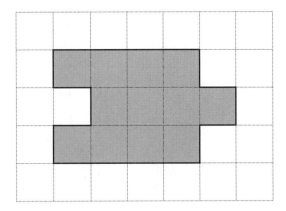

Exercise 7.7A _____

1 Estimate the area of each of these shapes.

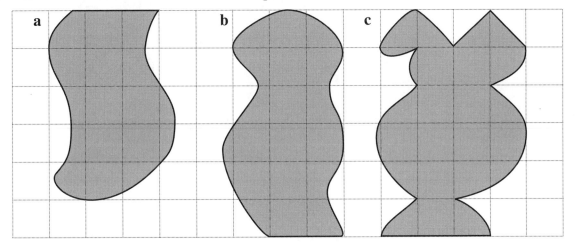

2 Find the area of each of these shapes by counting squares.

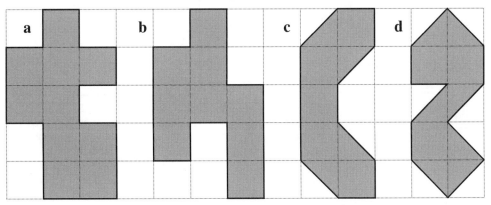

Exercise 7.7B

1   Estimate the area of each of these shapes.

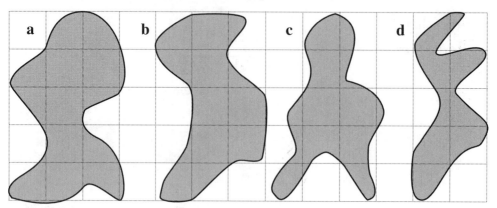

2   Find the area of each of these shapes by counting squares.

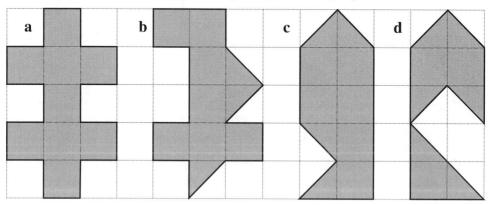

The area of a rectangle

▶ The formula for the area of a rectangle is:

Area = Length × Width

The area of ABCD is given by:

$$\text{Area} = 6 \times 4$$
$$= 24$$

The area of rectangle ABCD is 24 cm².

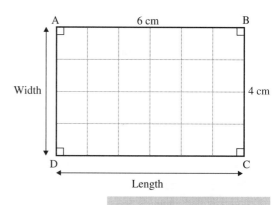

The width of a rectangle might be called the breadth.

Exercise 7.7C

1 Find the area of each of these shapes. The first four can
be checked by counting squares.

a
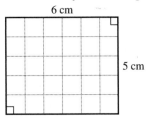
6 cm

5 cm

b
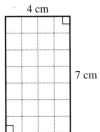
4 cm

7 cm

c
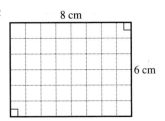
8 cm

6 cm

d
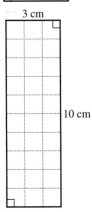
3 cm

10 cm

e
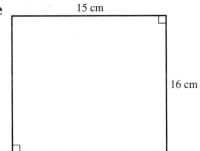
15 cm

16 cm

f
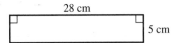
28 cm

5 cm

g
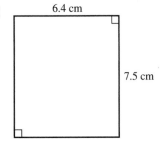
6.4 cm

7.5 cm

h
8.7 cm

9.8 cm

i
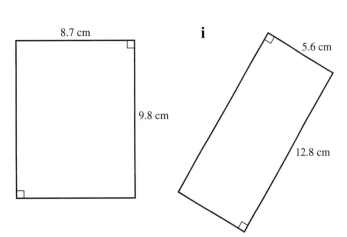
5.6 cm

12.8 cm

2 Find the area of each of these shapes.

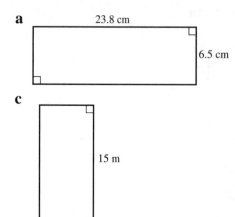

a 23.8 cm   6.5 cm

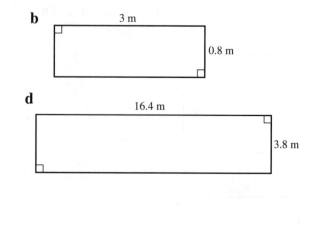

b 3 m   0.8 m

c 15 m   0.85 m

d 16.4 m   3.8 m

Exercise 7.7D

1 Calculate the area of each of these shapes.

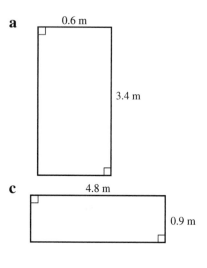

a 0.6 m   3.4 m

b 0.7 m   0.8 m

c 4.8 m   0.9 m

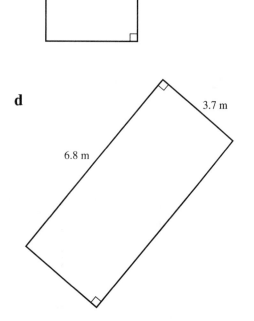

d 3.7 m   6.8 m

2 A page in a book is 120 mm long and 75 mm wide.
Calculate the area of the page.

3 The glass in a window is 42.5 cm long and 24.8 cm wide.
Calculate the area of the pane of glass.

4 A wall is in the shape of a rectangle.
The wall is to be painted white.
The wall is 44.6 metres long and 1.88 metres high.
Calculate the area to be painted.

> The height of a rectangle is the same as the width of the rectangle.

5 A poster on a bus is 3.35 metres long and 75 cm high.
Calculate the area of the poster.

> You need to work in the same units. So choose cm or metres to work in.

7.8 Nets of 3-D shapes

One way to show a 3-D shape on a sheet of paper is to draw the **net** of a shape.
The net shows what the shape would be like if it was unfolded and flattened.

Example 1 Draw the net of a cube.

This is the net of a cube:

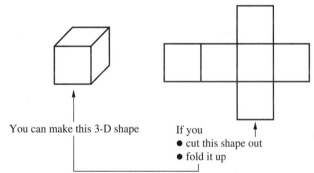

You can make this 3-D shape   If you
● cut this shape out
● fold it up

Example 2 Draw the net of a cylinder.

This is the net of a cylinder:

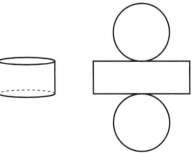

Exercise 7.8A

1 Sketch a net for each of these shapes

   a    **b**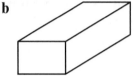

2 Copy this net on to a square grid.

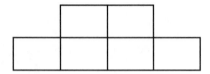

   Cut the net out.

   Can you fold your net to make a cube?
   Explain your answer.

3 Draw 2 **different** nets for a cube.
   Do not use this net: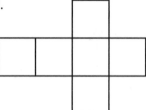

Exercise 7.8B

1 Sketch a net for each of these shapes.

   a 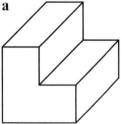   **b**

2 Make an accurate model of a cuboid that is 5 cm long,
   6 cm high and 10 cm deep.

3 Draw the net of both parts of a box of matches.

3 **a** Draw the net of a box to hold 8 dice.
   b Make your box.

7.9 The volume of a cuboid

The volume of a 3-D shape is the measure of how much
space it takes up.
Volume is given in cubic units, for example centimetres
cubed (cm^3) and metres cubed (m^3).

Example 1

What is the volume
of this cuboid?

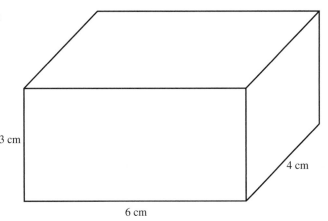

Image the cuboid is made
up of 1 cm cubes.

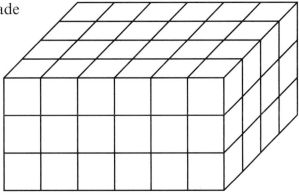

As you can't see all the cubes you might find it easier to
think of the cubes in layers:

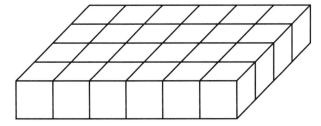

this layer has 24 cubes

There are 3 layers like this so there must be $24 + 24 + 24$ cubes $= 72$ cubes

You say the volume of the cuboid is $72 \, cm^3$.

Exercise 7.9A

1 Calculate the volume of each cuboid

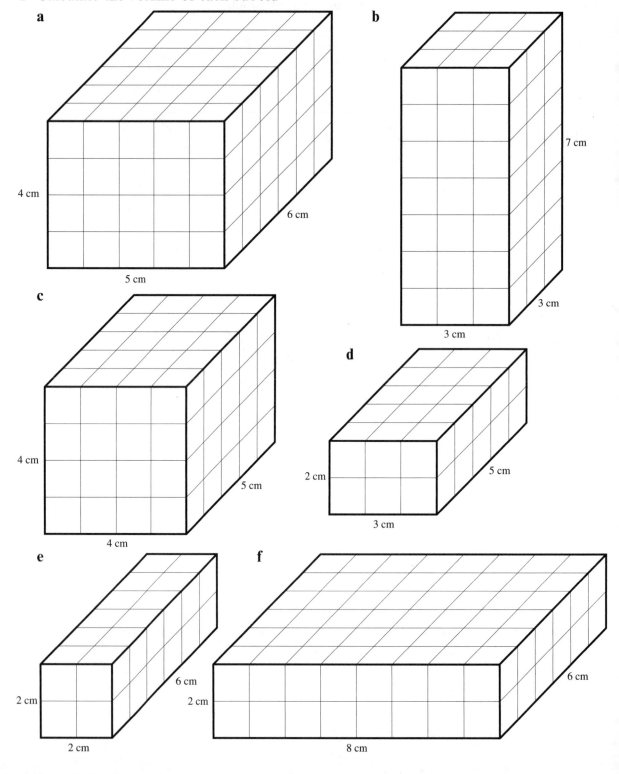

Exercise 7.9B

1 Calculate the volume of each cuboid

a

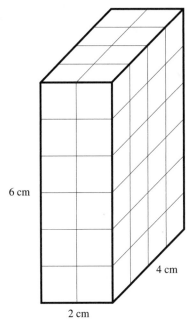

6 cm

4 cm

2 cm

b

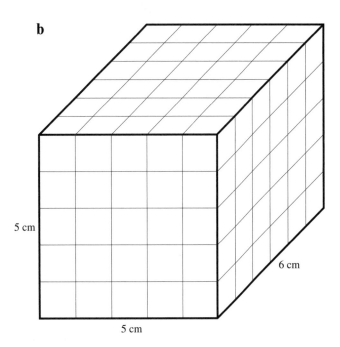

5 cm

6 cm

5 cm

c

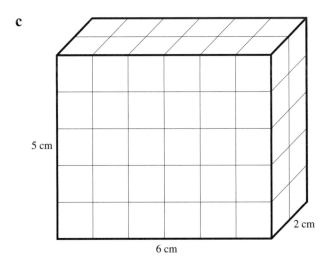

5 cm

2 cm

6 cm

d

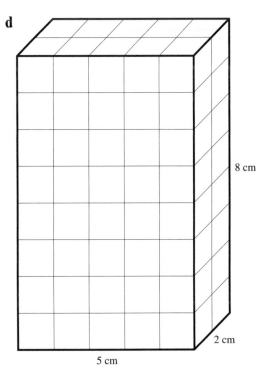

8 cm

2 cm

5 cm

e

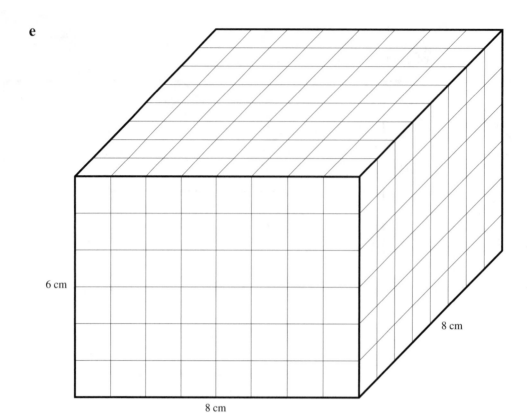

6 cm

8 cm

8 cm

f

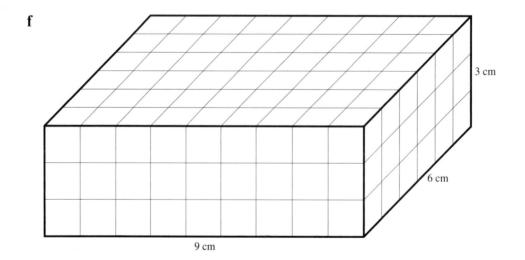

3 cm

6 cm

9 cm

7.10 Circumference of a circle

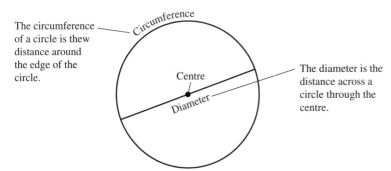

The circumference of a circle is thew distance around the edge of the circle.

Circumference

Centre

Diameter

The diameter is the distance across a circle through the centre.

▶ The circumference of a circle is roughly 3× the diameter.

Example 1

Estimate the circumference of a circle with diameter 12 cm.

Circumference is roughly $3 \times$ diameter
$$= 3 \times 12 \text{ cm}$$
$$= 36 \text{ cm}$$

So, the circumference of a circle with diameter 12 cm is roughly 36 cm.

Exercise 7.10A

1 Estimate the circumference of each circle.

   a diameter 8 cm   b diameter 15 cm   c diameter 6.5 cm
   d diameter 14 cm   e diameter 16.5 cm   f diameter 7 metres

2 A circle has a circumference that is roughly 51 cm.
   Estimate the diameter of the circle.

Exercise 7.10B

1 Copy and complete this table

Circle	Diameter	Estimate of circumference
a	6 cm	
b	19 cm	
c	20.5 cm	
d	35 cm	
e	19.5 cm	
f	36.5 cm	
g	0.8 cm	
h	6.2 cm	
i	76 cm	
j	125 cm	

2 Darren has a piece of rope 45 metres long.
Estimate the diameter of the largest circle he can make
with the rope.

3 The second hand of a watch is 18 mm long.
How far does the top of the second hand travel in 60
seconds?
(Hint: you may need to draw a sketch because you need
to think about the diameter.)

Revision Exercise 7

Review

1 Give the value shown by each arrow on the scale.

Unit 7.1

2 Estimate the value shown by the arrows on each scale.

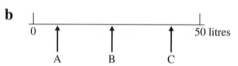

Unit 7.1

3 Give each of these lengths in centimetres.
  a 1.4 m   **b** 2.6 m   **c** 12.5 m   **d** 0.4 m   **e** 0.08 m

Unit 7.2

4 Give each of these weight in grams (g).
  a 5 kg   **b** 3.5 kg   **c** 2.6 kg   **d** 6.03 kg **e** 0.45 kg

Unit 7.2

5 Give each of these weights in ounces (oz).
  a 2 lb   **b** $1\frac{1}{2}$ lb   **c** $3\frac{1}{4}$ lb   **d** $\frac{3}{4}$ lb   **e** $2\frac{1}{4}$ lb

Unit 7.2

6 A baker uses 265 lb of flour to make loaves.
What is this weight in kilograms?

Unit 7.3

7 On holiday last year Cora cycled 134 miles.
What is this distance in kilometres?

Unit 7.3

8 A heating oil tank holds 280 gallons of oil.
How many litres is this?

Unit 7.3

9 This is a conversion graph for ounces to grams.   *Review*

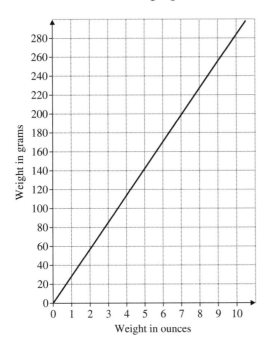

Use the conversion graph to answer these.

a A bird weights 180 g. Give this weight in ounces.
b A recipe uses 7 oz of currants. How many grams is this?
c A young hare was found to weigh 12 oz. What is this weight in grams?   *Unit 7.4*

10 This graph shows the temperature inside a coach.

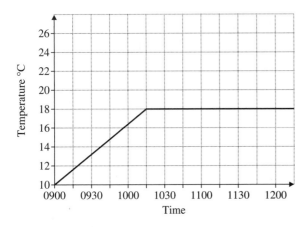

a Estimate the temperature in the coach at these times.
  0930   0945   1045   1110
b Estimate the time when the temperature was 15°C.   *Unit 7.4*

11 This graph shows the journey of a car.
It goes from Corley to Sibley and back again.

Review

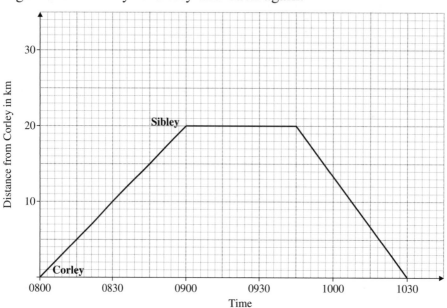

  a At what time was the car 10 km from Corley?
  b How long was the car parked at Sibley?
  c Which was quicker: the journey to Sibley or the return journey?   *Unit 7.4*

12 Maria went on holiday for 6 weeks. How many days was this?   *Unit 7.5*

13 How many hours are there in one week?   *Unit 7.5*

14 Give each of these times in the 24-hour clock system.
  a 3 am   **b** 4 pm   **c** 5.30 am   **d** 7.15 pm   **e** 9.45 pm   *Unit 7.5*

15 Give each of these times using **am** or **pm**.
  a 14.50   **b** 06.20   **c** 02.55   **d** 21.25   **e** 23.40   *Unit 7.5*

16 Calculate the perimeter of each of these shapes.

  a

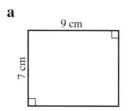

  b

  c

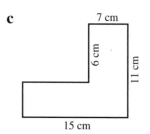

Unit 7.6

17 Calculate the perimeter of each of these shapes.

a

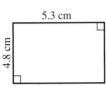

5.3 cm

4.8 cm

b

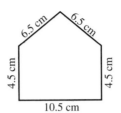

6.5 cm   6.5 cm

4.5 cm   4.5 cm

10.5 cm

c

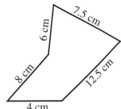

7.5 cm

6 cm

8 cm

12.5 cm

4 cm

Unit 7.6

18 Find the area of each of these shapes.

a

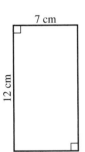

7 cm

12 cm

b

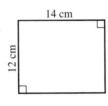

14 cm

12 cm

c

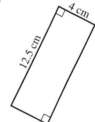

4 cm

12.5 cm

Unit 7.7

19 Calculate the areas of each of these shapes.

a

7 cm

12.4 cm

b

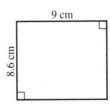

9 cm

8.6 cm

c

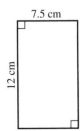

7.5 cm

12 cm

d

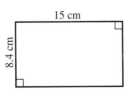

15 cm

8.4 cm

Unit 7.7

Review

20 Sketch a net of a cylinder.   *Unit 7.8*

21 Sketch a net of a cube.   *Unit 7.8*

22 Draw an accurate net for this prism.

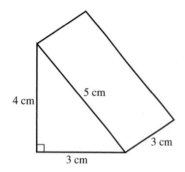

Unit 7.8

23 Find the volume of each solid.

a

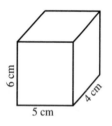

b

c

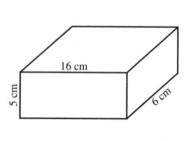

Unit 7.9

24 Estimate the circumference of a circle with diameter 8 cm.   *Unit 7.10*

25 A circle has a circumference of 45 cm. Estimate its diameter.   *Unit 7.10*

8 PLANNING AND COLLECTING DATA

8.1 Collecting data

Data is another word for information.
It often involves counting, or it may involve measuring
a length, a weight or a time.

Before you collect data you need to decide what you want to find out.
Then you have to decide how to collect the data.

There are a number of ways to do this.
One way is to design a data collection sheet. It looks like this:

Southway Sports Centre
Western Avenue
Crofton
CR6 9BY

Southway Sports Centre

NEW MEMBER

Name _____

Address _____

Post code ▢▢▢▢ ▢▢▢   Telephone ▢▢▢▢▢▢▢▢▢▢▢

Please debit my Access/Visa Card by the amount of £ _____

Card number ▢▢▢▢▢▢▢▢▢▢▢▢▢▢▢▢

Expiry date ▢▢/▢▢

Or I enclose a cheque made payable to SSC for the amount of £ _____

I wish my membership to start on ▢▢▢▢▢▢ (Date)

Signature

Date ▢▢/▢▢/▢▢

For Centre use only   Membership number ▢▢▢▢▢▢▢

This data collection form is a quick and easy way to record
and hold data.
The important thing is that it collects data on the same
things from everyone.

Exercise 8.1A

1   List all different pieces of data collected by this sheet.

2   Which piece of data on the form is not collected from the new member?

3   Design a data collection sheet that could be used to order T-shirts by post.
    There are two sizes, L and XL, they cost £8.99 each, and they can be red, yellow or blue.

Exercise 8.1B

1   Design a data collection sheet for people booking seats at a cinema by post.
    The seats cost £4.75, £5.25 or £6.50.
    Showings are at 16.00, 19.00, 21.50 and 01.00.

2   Imagine you run a long-stay car park charging £3.85 per day.
    Design a data collection sheet to send out to customers who want to book a space.

You can design a data collection sheet where questions have to be answered.
The simplest type is where you just answer Yes or No.

> You must think about the questions to ask.

This is part of a Customer data collection sheet.

	Customer Choices	Yes	No
1.	Are you over 30 years of age?	☐	☐
2.	Do you shop every day?	☐	☐
3.	Do you always buy bread when you visit this supermarket?	☐	☐
4.	Do you have a Saver Card?	☐	☐
5.	Do you use our delivery service?	☐	☐
6.	Do you have children?	☐	☐
7.			

Exercise 8.1C

1 Design three more questions for the sheet.

2 Why are these questions no good for the Customer Choices sheet?

   a How often do you eat fish?
   b Do you like fish?

3 Design three Yes/No questions for data collection about how people travel to work.

Exercise 8.1D

1 Why is this not a good Yes/No question on a travel to work data sheet?

     Can you ride a bike?   Yes/No

2 You want to pick out customers in their 20s in your data.

   a Why is 'How old are you?' not a good question?
   b Write a better question. Give reasons why you think it is better.

3 Design three Yes/No questions for data collection about what people watch on TV.

You can use a data collection sheet that has questions and multi-choice lists.

5.   Which of these TV channels do you watch most?

      Please tick only one box.

           BBC 1   ☐

           BBC 2   ☐

           Channel 4   ☐

           Other   ☐

Exercise 8.1E _____

1 Design two other multi-choice questions to collect data from TV viewers.

2 Design three multi-choice questions to collect data about travel to school.

Exercise 8.1F _____

1 Design three multi-choice questions to collect data about home computers.

2 Choose a subject you want to find information about. Design three multi-choice questions to collect data.

8.2 Frequency tables

The data you collect is often put into a table.
This is called a **frequency table**.

> A frequency table shows how frequently some event happened.

Exercise 8.2A _____

This frequency table gives results from a health survey.

Type of exercise taken

	Gym	Cycling	Walking	Running	Swimming	None
Females	12	8	34	7	17	22
Males	37	4	8	15	11	25

1 How many females exercised by cycling?

2 How many males took no exercise?

3 Give the most popular exercise taken:
   a by the females   **b** by the males.

4 Copy and complete:

   The fraction of females who chose walking or running was $\dfrac{\Box}{100}$.

5 Copy and complete:

The fraction of males who took some exercise was $\dfrac{\square}{100}$.

6 For females which exercise was least popular?

Exercise 8.2B _____

This frequency table gives data about visits to a store in one week.

Number of visits

	1	2	3	4	More than 4
Females	6	34	25	11	14
Males	14	19	24	8	25

1 How many females are shown in the table?

2 From the frequency table showing visits to the store in one week:

   a how many females visited the store three times?
   b how many males made less than three visits?

3 a How many males are shown in the table?
   b What fraction of the males made four visits in the one week?

4 a How many females made two or four visits?
   b What fraction of the females made two or four visits?

5 a How many men made more than one visit to the store?
   b What fraction of the men was this?

▶ You can construct a frequency table from raw data.
Raw data is data that has not been ordered in any way.

Example

Make a frequency table to show this data for the number of passengers in 50 cars.

   1, 3, 0, 4, 0, 1, 2, 3, 2, 0, 4, 0, 5, 0, 1, 1, 1, 2, 6, 3, 4, 5,
   2, 0, 0, 4, 0, 1, 2, 1, 4, 5, 7, 6, 0, 3, 2, 1, 1, 5, 2, 3, 1, 0,
   7, 0, 3, 4, 1, 1.

In the frequency table you need to show:

- the classes for the data – in this case the number of passengers: 0, 1, 2, ..., 7.
- the frequency for each class.

You may also show your tally marks.

Number of passengers	Tally	Frequency
0	ЖТ ЖТ I	11
1	ЖТ ЖТ II	12
2	ЖТ II	7
3	ЖТ I	6
4	ЖТ I	6
5	IIII	4
6	II	2
7	II	2

Group your tally marks in 5's like this: ЖТ so they are easier to count.

Check that the frequency column adds up to the total amount of data collected:
$$11 + 12 + 7 + 6 + 6 + 4 + 2 + 2 = 50$$

Exercise 8.2C

1 Look at this data.

The number of letters delivered to each house in North Street
0, 1, 1, 2, 1, 1, 0, 0, 0, 4, 3, 4, 2, 3, 1, 1, 0, 0, 1, 0, 3, 0, 4, 5, 1, 0, 1, 0, 1, 2, 1, 2,
2, 3, 1, 0, 0, 4, 1, 2, 0, 1, 2, 0, 1, 0, 2, 2, 0, 0, 2, 3, 5, 1, 6, 4, 2, 1, 1, 1

a Copy and complete this frequency table.

Number of letters	Tally	Frequency
0		17
⋮		

b How many houses are there in North Street?
c How many houses had no letters delivered?
d How many houses had three or more letters delivered?
e How many houses had no more than two letters delivered?

2 a Make a frequency table for this data.

The amount spent by players on the Lottery in one shop

£1, £3, £4, £1, £4, £9, £3, £5, £5, £7, £1, £1, £1, £3, £12,
£10, £4, £5, £1, £2, £2, £4, £7, £2, £5, £8, £10, £2, £1, £1,
£1, £7, £15, £2, £2, £5, £3, £4, £1, £1, £1, £4, £5, £2, £3,
£2, £1, £1, £4, £5, £10, £1, £1, £5, £1, £1, £8, £1, £2, £3

> In your table you must include each class between the least and most in the data. Here include all classes from £1 to £15.

b How many players spent £10 or more?
c How many players spent less than £5?
d How many players spent exactly £9?
e How many players are shown by the table?

Exercise 8.2D _____

1 a Make a frequency table to show this data.

Scores from rolling a 0 to 9 dice

3, 5, 6, 3, 2, 8, 9, 4, 0, 3, 0, 1, 6, 7, 3, 4, 8, 1, 0, 0, 2, 4,
1, 0, 5, 3, 8, 9, 5, 2, 1, 7, 3, 4, 0, 7, 1, 4, 2, 0, 3, 6, 1, 5,
8, 5, 2, 3, 1, 1, 4, 1, 9, 6, 0, 4, 0, 5, 0, 0

> This data has been collected by doing an experiment.

b How many single pieces of data are shown by your frequency table?
c What was the frequency of a score of 7?
d What was the frequency for a score of at least 6?
e Give the frequency for a score of 5 or less.

2 In an experiment students took a handful of cubes from a bag.
The cubes were counted and returned to the bag.
Here are the results:

Number of cubes taken

5, 8, 12, 6, 8, 6, 9, 10, 12, 11, 7, 9, 7, 12, 15, 14, 9, 10, 11, 11,
7, 8, 5, 7, 9, 9, 6, 10, 11, 9, 6, 8, 8, 9, 9, 11, 8, 9, 12, 14, 10, 7,
8, 7, 9, 8, 6, 7, 10, 11, 9, 8, 9, 10, 10, 7, 9, 11, 8, 6, 9, 9, 10

a Make a frequency table to show this data.
b What was the largest number of cubes taken in one handful?
c Give the frequency for ten or more cubes.
d Give the frequency for fewer than nine cubes taken.
e Which number of cubes had the highest frequency?
f How many times was the experiment repeated?

8.3 Grouped data

If your data is widely spread it can help to group the data. When you group data into classes, each class should have the same interval or size.

Classes of 1 to 5 and 6 to 10 are equal class intervals.

> A class interval gives the spread of the class.
> A class of 1 to 5 has an interval of 4.
> A class of 6 to 10 has an interval of 4.

Example

This data gives the age of people visiting a library.
Make a frequency table for the data using class intervals:
11 to 20, 21 to 30, 31 to 40, 41 to 50, 51 to 60, 61 to 70, 71 to 80.

Age of people visiting the library

22, 35, 21, 18, 45, 62, 71, 19, 17, 19, 37, 44, 56, 58, 41,
63, 55, 20, 61, 48, 12, 19, 23, 48, 31, 54, 76, 39, 40, 55,
61, 72, 70, 17, 15, 14, 17, 19, 27, 31, 32, 37, 45, 67, 54,
19, 16, 14, 18, 63, 20, 60, 44, 71, 37, 16, 16, 21, 21, 30

Age (class)	Tally	Frequency
11 to 20	|||| |||| |||| |||| ||||	19
21 to 30	|||| ||	7
31 to 40	|||| ||||	9
41 to 50	|||| ||	7
51 to 60	|||| ||	7
61 to 70	|||| ||	7
71 to 80	||||	4

> The disadvantage of grouping data is you cannot tell the frequency of a single piece of data. Here, you cannot say how many 15-year-olds visited the library.

Exercise 8.3A

1 A group of students were asked how long, in seconds, they spent cleaning their teeth. Here are their responses:

   16, 22, 25, 31, 40, 42, 12, 15, 26, 22, 34, 28, 19, 48,
   35, 27, 19, 50, 15, 22, 53, 18, 17, 29, 31, 28, 38, 42,
   19, 51, 39, 41, 35, 22, 15, 24

   a Make a grouped frequency table for the data.
     Use groups of: 1 to 10, 11 to 20, 21 to 30, 31 to 40, 41 to 50, 51 to 60.
   b The frequency table show the data for how many students?
   c Which class had the highest frequency?
   d Which class had the lowest frequency?
   e How many students spent 30 seconds or less cleaning their teeth?

2 Use the data for 'The amount spent by players on the Lottery' on page 185.

   a Make a grouped frequency table to show the data.
      Use groups of £1 to £4, £5 to £8, £9 to £12, £13 to £16.
   b Which class had the highest frequency?
   c Which class had the lowest frequency?

3 This data shows the number of passengers leaving each bus at the bus station.

      15, 2, 22, 34, 6, 8, 14, 15, 29, 1, 42, 38, 19, 7, 2, 4, 0,
      19, 51, 33, 25, 42, 18, 6, 21, 30, 47, 17, 19, 6, 18, 7, 9,
      22, 46, 20, 15, 7, 9

   a Make a grouped frequency table to show the data.
      Use groups of: 0 to 9, 10 to 19, 20 to 29, 30 to 39,
      40 to 49, 50 to 59.
   b How many buses had less than 30 passengers leaving at the bus station?
   c Which class had the highest frequency?

4 Use the data for question **3** above.

   a Make a grouped frequency table for the data.
      This time use groups of:
      0 to 14, 15 to 29, 30 to 44, 45 to 59.
   b Which class had the lowest frequency?

Exercise 8.3B _____

1 This data gives the length in cm of beans after 72 days for beans planted at the same time.

      8.6, 12.3, 5.8, 14.7, 4.2, 11.5, 17.6, 14.4, 15, 16.3,
      11.7, 10, 8.2, 14.8, 16.5, 7.6, 15.8, 14.3, 9.8, 18.2,
      16.3, 14.5, 13.8, 14, 12.6

   a Make a grouped frequency table for the data.
      Use groups of: 0 to 4.9 cm, 5 cm to 9.9 cm,
      10 cm to 14.9 cm and 15 cm to 19.9 cm.
   b Which class had the highest frequency?

2 At a Customer Service desk the time taken in seconds to deal with each customer is recorded. This is the data for one shift:

> 12.5, 16, 23.4, 35.6, 9, 12.5, 44.8, 57.3, 15.5, 56.4, 42,
> 31.5, 38, 57.5, 78.4, 88, 23.5, 19, 12.6, 26.5, 67.2,
> 74.3, 14, 27.8, 35.2, 63, 59, 72, 28.5

a Make a grouped frequency table for the data.
Use groups of: 0 to 9.9 s, 10 s to 19.9 s, 20 s to 29.9 s,
..., ..., 80 s to 89.9 s

b Which class had the highest frequency?

c Which class had a frequency of 3?

d How many calls were less than 40 seconds?

e Make a different grouped frequency table for the data.
Use groups of: 0 to 19.9 s, 20 s to 39.9 s, 40 s to 59.9 s,
..., ..., 80 s to 99.9 s.

f Which class has a frequency of 6 in this frequency table?

Revision Exercise 8

Review

1 Design a data collection sheet that could be used to order sweatshirts by post.
There are three sizes: L, XL and XXL.
There are four colours: red, blue, black and yellow.
They cost £14.99 each.

Unit 8.1

2 These are yes/no questions used on a data collection sheet:
Do you own a bicycle?
How often do you cycle?

a Which question do you think works?

b Rewrite the question you think does not work so that it does work.

Unit 8.1

3 Design a multi-choice question for a survey on favourite snacks.

Unit 8.1

4 This tables gives the results from a travel survey in a school:

Review

	Type of travel to and from school					
	Bus	Cycle	car	Taxi	Walk	Train
Male	16	22	31	19	7	5
Female	21	8	16	9	35	11

  a How many males walked to school?
  b How many females cycled to school?
  c What was the most popular type of travel to school for females?
  d How did most males travel to school?
  e What fraction of females cycled to school?
  f What fraction of males took the bus to school?

Unit 8.2

5 This data shows the scores on a 1 to 6 dice.

  3, 5, 4, 6, 3, 2, 4, 1, 5, 1, 1, 2, 3, 4, 5, 2, 3, 1,
  6, 6, 5, 1, 2, 1, 6, 1, 2, 3, 2, 5, 1, 6, 2, 3, 5, 1,
  2, 1, 5, 3, 4, 1, 2, 1, 6, 3, 2, 4, 1, 5, 6, 6

  a Make a frequency table for the data.
  b What was the frequency of a score of 2?
  c Which score had the highest frequency?
  d Which score had the lowest frequency?

Unit 8.2

6 This data gives the time (in seconds) it took to answer a call at a call centre.

  15, 23, 18, 27, 18, 35, 19, 22, 38, 46, 24, 29, 33,
  41, 42, 38, 36, 18, 21, 27, 44, 38, 29, 45, 19, 22,
  25, 39, 38, 41, 24, 45, 26, 23, 37, 35, 30, 28

  a Make a grouped frequency table for the data.
    Use groups of 15 to 24, 25 to 34, 35 to 44, 45 to 54
    seconds.
  b The frequency table gives data for how many calls?
  c Which class had the highest frequency?
  d Which class had the lowest frequency?
  e How many calls took at least 25 seconds to answer?
  f How many calls took less than 35 seconds to answer?

Unit 8.3

9 REPRESENTING AND INTERPRETING DATA

9.1 Frequency diagrams

A frequency diagram is a way of showing data with a graph.
There are different types of frequency diagram:

Bar charts

▶ A bar chart uses bars to represent data.

This bar chart shows the data from the frequency table.

Frequency table

Shoe size	Frequency
2	2
3	10
4	12
5	15
6	18
7	25
8	18

Vertical bar chart

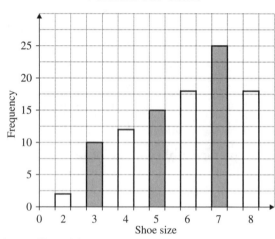

Or you can draw a horizontal bar chart like this:

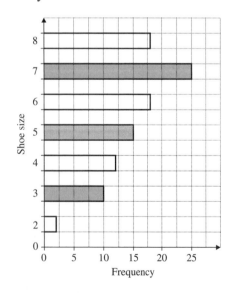

Remember to label your graph so that anyone else can understand it.

Pictograms

▶ A pictogram uses a symbol to stand for a number of pieces of data:

Frequency table

Size	Frequency
2	4
3	4
4	6
5	8
6	12
7	10

Pictogram

Size	
2	▭
3	▭
4	▭ ▫
5	▭ ▭
6	▭ ▭ ▭
7	▭ ▭ ▫

▭ = 4 pairs of shoes

> You must give a key for your symbol.

> If a block stands for 4 pairs then half a block stands for 2 pairs.

Exercise 9.1A

1 This data shows the number of cars using a car wash.

Day	Frequency of use
Monday	8
Tuesday	16
Wednesday	12
Thursday	9
Friday	14
Saturday	24
Sunday	28

> Remember to show the frequency your symbol stands for.

  a Show this data on a bar chart.
  b Draw a pictogram for the data.

2 This bar chart shows the data for the number of empty crisp packets in the bin at the end of each day.

  a How many packets were there on Tuesday?
  b What was the frequency for Sunday?
  c Make a frequency table for the data shown by the bar chart.
  d Show the data with a pictogram.

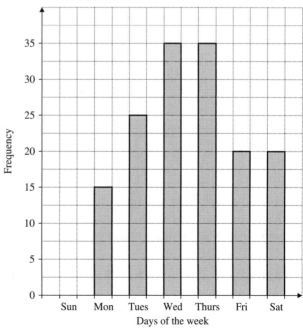

Graph to show the number of crisp packets in a bin at the end of the day

Exercise 9.1B _____

1 This pictogram shows the data for the number of cars in
a car park at noon each day.

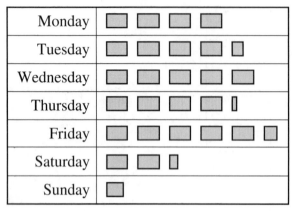

Monday	▢ ▢ ▢ ▢
Tuesday	▢ ▢ ▢ ▢ ▯
Wednesday	▢ ▢ ▢ ▢ ▢
Thursday	▢ ▢ ▢ ▢ ▮
Friday	▢ ▢ ▢ ▢ ▢ ▯
Saturday	▢ ▢ ▮
Sunday	▢

▢ = 10 cars

a How many cars were there on Wednesday?
b On which day were there most cars?
c Estimate the frequency for each day and make a
frequency table for the data.
d Use your frequency table to draw a bar chart for the data.

2 This data shows the frequency of passengers using a river
ferry crossing one day.

Passengers

Crossing number	Frequency
1	12
2	24
3	32
4	16
5	20

> Remember to show the
> frequency your symbol
> stands for.

a Show the data with a bar chart.
b Show the data with a pictogram.
c In total, how many passengers used the ferry in all five
crossings?
d Explain why your bar chart might be more accurate
than your pictogram.

9.2 Line graphs

Line graphs can be used to show a set of data. Here are two types:

Bar line graphs

This bar line graph shows the data in the table.

Time	Temperature (°C)
08.00	78
08.30	78.4
09.00	78.2
09.30	78.8
10.00	79
10.30	79.3
11.00	78.5

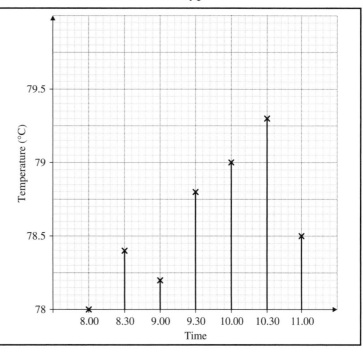

Line graphs

This line graph shows the data in the table.

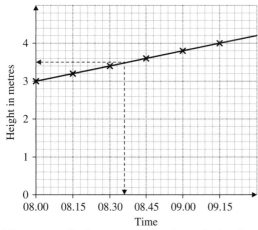

Time	Height (metres)
08.00	3
08.15	3.2
08.30	3.4
08.45	3.6
09.00	3.8
09.15	4.0

You can find more data than is in the table.
From the graph you can read off a height for the water at any time between 08.00 and 09.15.
From the graph the height of the water at 08.36 was about 3.5 metres.

Remember when you read data from a graph you only get an estimated value.

Exercise 9.2A _____

1 A gardener decided to measure a growing sunflower every
   five days.
   The table gives the data collected.

Number of days	Height (cm)
0	16
5	19
10	23.5
15	27
20	31.5
25	36
30	40
35	46
40	52.5
45	55

   a Draw a bar line graph to show this data.
   b Draw a line graph for the data.
   c From your line graph copy and complete this table
      with estimates for each ☐.

Remember:
A bar line graph and a
line graph are different.
Make sure you know
which one is which.

Height	Number of days
☐	8
☐	22
42 cm	☐
☐	12
☐	36
25 cm	☐

2 This bar line graph shows the amount of fuel in the tank
   of a beach cleaner.
   Readings were recorded every ten minutes.

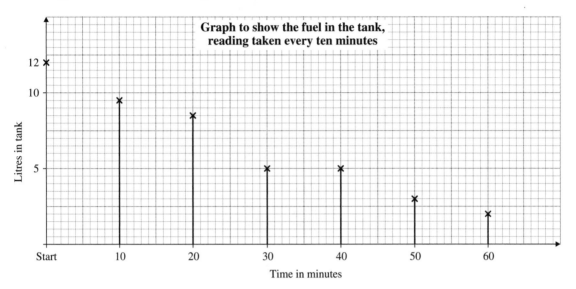

a Put the data shown by the bar line graph in a table.
b Show the data as a line graph.
c From your line graph, copy and complete this table
   with estimates for the height.

Fuel (litres)	Minutes	Fuel (litres)	Minutes
☐	6	☐	14
☐	25	☐	32
☐	48	☐	57

Exercise 9.2B _____

1 The depth of a bore hole is measured every ten minutes.
   The table gives the data collected.

Time (min)	0	10	20	30	40	50	60	70	80
Depth (m)	0	2.4	3.5	4.2	5.6	7	8.4	9.6	10

a Draw a bar line graph to show this data.
b Show the data with a line graph.

c From your line graph copy and complete this table
with an estimate for each ☐.

Time (min)	Depth (m)	Time (min)	Depth (m)
12	☐	25	☐
33	☐	38	☐
☐	6	☐	8

2 This bar line graph shows the length of carpet produced
by a weaving machine. The length, in metres, is measured
every 20 minutes.

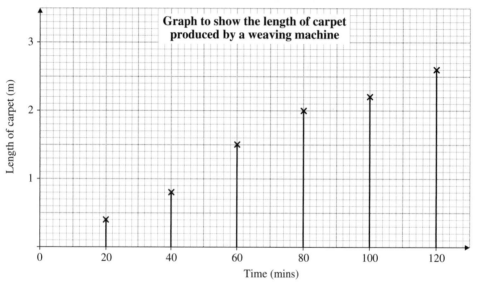

a Show the data in the bar line graph with a table.
b Draw a line graph to show the data.
c From your line graph, copy and complete this table
with estimates for each missing item of data.

Time (min)	Length (m)	Time (min)	Length (m)
10	☐	16	☐
28	☐	45	☐
☐	1	☐	1.4
☐	2	☐	2.4

9.3 Pie charts

▶ A pie chart is a frequency diagram that uses a circle to display data.

You divide the circle into sectors showing the proportions of the total in each class.

Example

This pie chart gives the colour of the first twenty cars in a car park.

You can see that:

- More cars were red than any other colour.
- About 5 cars were white.
- More than half the cars were red or blue.

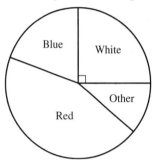

Pie chart to show the colour of the first twenty cars in a car park

Exercise 9.3A _____

1 This pie chart shows the number of visits made to a cinema by 40 people.

   a What was the greatest number of visits?
   b Roughly how many people made 3 visits?
   c Roughly how many people made 1 visit?

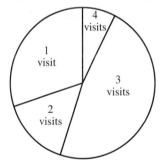

Number of visits to a cinema

2 This pie chart shows the favourite drink of 100 people.

   a What was the most popular drink?
   b What was the least popular drink?
   c List the drinks in order from least popular to most popular.
   d Roughly how many chose cola?

Favourite drinks

3 This pie chart shows the favourite holiday destination of 1000 people.

  a Where was most popular?

  b List the destinations in order from least popular to most popular.

  c Roughly how many people chose France?

Favourite holiday

Exercise 9.3B

1 This pie chart shows the type of TV programmes watched by 200 people.

  a What type was least popular?

  b List the types in order from most popular to least popular.

  c Roughly how many people watched TV Soaps?

TV programmes watched

2 This pie chart shows the makes of car sold by a dealer last month. The chart shows 300 cars.

  a Which make was most popular?

  b Which make had roughly the same sales as Rover?

  c List the makes in order from least sales to most sales.

  d Roughly how many Renault cars were sold?

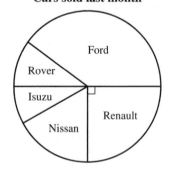

Cars sold last month

3 This pie chart gives the results of a survey of the sun block used by people on holiday. The pie chart shows 4000 people.

  a Roughly how many people use no sunblock?

  b Roughly how many people use Factor 15 or more?

  c What sunblock is used most by this group?

  d From this data can you say which sunblock is most popular in Blackpool?
    Give reasons for your answer.

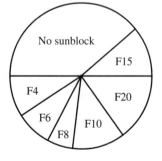

Sunblock used

9.4 Averages

▶ An average is a single value that is typical of a set of data.
There are three types of average:

- mode
- median
- mean.

Mode

▶ The mode is the most common value.

This data shows the shoe size of 50 people.

Shoe size	2	3	**4**	5	6	7	8	9
Frequency	4	11	**15**	14	3	2	1	0

The **mode** for this data is shoe size 4.
Shoe size 4 has a frequency of 15.

> The modal value is the value with the highest frequency.

Median

▶ The median is the middle value when the data is arranged in size order.

Example 1

Find the median of each set of data:

a 5, 7, 1, 2, 8, 5, 8, 3, 4, 9, 5, 8, 4, 10, 7
b 15, 14, 17, 11, 15, 9, 19, 10, 12, 11, 9, 20

> Most mistakes finding the median are made because people do not put the data in order before they look for the median value.

a Order the data: 1, 2, 3, 4, 4, 5, 5, **5**, 7, 7, 8, 8, 8, 9, 10
                    7 values   ↑   7 values
                       This is the middle value.

The median is 5.

Note: As there are 15 pieces of data, the median value is the 8th item in the order.

> When you put your data set in order you must include each item of data – even repeated values.

b Order the data: 9, 9, 10, 11, 11, 12, 14, 15, 15, 17, 19, 20
                    6 values   ↑   6 values
               The middle value is half way between 12 and 14.

> Remember to include repeated values.

The median is half way between 12 and 14.
So the median is 13.

> The median does not have to be one of the values.

Note: There are 12 pieces of data in this set, so the median value is between the 6th and 7th items of data in order.

Exercise 9.4A

1 These are the marks for a group in a test.

> Mark: 8, 6, 9, 11, 10, 11, 7, 8, 6, 9, 11

  a What is the mode for this data set?
  b How many pieces of data are there?
  c Find the median mark.

2 The length of some bean pods are measured:

> Length (cm):   11, 12, 9, 12, 10, 11, 13, 12, 12, 11, 8, 14, 5

  a How many pieces of data are in the set?
  b Find the median mark.
  c Find the mode for this data set.

3 People on buses at the bus stop were counted. This is the data:

> People: 8, 12, 24, 9, 3, 4, 16, 11, 14, 15, 2, 14, 6, 17

  a How many pieces of data are in the set?
  b What number of people is the mode?
  c Find the median for the data.

4 Find the mode and median for each of these data sets.

  a 6, 12, 4, 5, 8, 19, 20, 16, 15, 8, 6, 4, 8, 12, 14
  b 3, 6, 4, 7, 4, 4, 5, 5, 6, 7, 4, 9, 6
  c 25, 33, 45, 55, 43, 2, 38, 5, 36, 46, 51, 45, 19, 6
  d 125, 98, 56, 75, 56, 88, 91, 56, 104, 56

Exercise 9.4B

1 Copy and complete this sentence.

> The mode of a set of data is . . . .

2 Copy and complete:

> To find the median:

  ● First you must . . . .

  ● Then you . . . .

3 The number of items in baskets at the checkout in a supermarket were recorded. This data shows the results.

4, 12, 5, 7, 3, 8, 4, 9, 11, 4, 16, 13, 4, 11, 4, 12

  a How many pieces of data are there?
  b Find the median number of items in a basket.
  c What is the mode for this data set?

4 Find the mode and median for each of these data sets.

  a 7, 12, 14, 9, 15, 18, 9, 16, 20, 18, 16, 11, 7, 9, 13
  b 325, 400, 443, 325, 340, 168, 848
  c 340, 280, 280, 960, 275, 144

Mean

▶ The mean for a set of data is a numerical value found by adding all the values in the set and dividing this total by the number of values.

> The mean may be called the arithmetic mean.

Example 2

Find the mean of this data set:

12, 15, 22, 17, 11, 39, 44, 28, 56, 71, 8, 15, 22, 34, 17

Add all the values:	$12 + 15 + 22 + \ldots + \ldots + 18 = 411$
The number of values is:	15
The mean is	$411 \div 15 = 27.4$

> Use a calculator for this.

So, the mean for the data set is 27.4

> The mean is a numerical value. It does not have to be a whole number or a number from the data set.

Note: When the term average is used, people take this as being the mean.
         Be careful, as you know the mean is just one type of average.

Range

▶ The **range** tells us how spread out a data set is.
    The range = the greatest value − the smallest value in a data set.

Example 3

Calculate the range for this data set.

13, 13, 24, 31, 16, 11, 35, 26, 16, 25, 26, 31, 20, 18, 31

To calculate the range:

The greatest value is: 35
The smallest value is: 11

The range = greatest value – smallest value

$$= 35 - 11$$
$$= 24$$

The range for the data set is 24.

Exercise 9.4C _____

1 Look at this data set.

   22, 17, 61, 44, 52, 38, 15, 32, 55, 31, 56

  a What is the greatest value?
  b What is the smallest value?
  c What is the range for the data set?

2 Look at this data set.

   15, 18, 6, 19, 34, 48, 34, 22, 36, 28

  a What is the largest value?
  b What is the range for the data set?

3 This data set has a range of 6.

   11, 14, ☐, 15, 13, 12, 12, 15, 15,

  a What is the smallest value?
  b What do you think the ☐ stands for?

4 A data set has a range of 122.
  The greatest value piece of data is 365.
  What is the smallest value in the set?

5 This data shows the number of tickets sold each day for a
  historic tram ride.

Day	M	T	W	Th	F	S	Su
Tickets	58	76	97	108	48	262	177

  a On which day were most tickets sold?
  b Which day had the lowest ticket sales?
  c Find the range for the data.

Exercise 9.4D _____

1 What is the range for this data set?

      26, 15, 74, 32, 27, 46, 32, 12, 56, 21, 3, 17

2 Calculate the range for this set of data.

      34.6, 27.2, 18.5, 24.3, 25.8, 18.5, 21.6, 24.3, 7.2

3 A data set has a range of 16.
The highest value is 55. What is the lowest value?
How many pieces of data are in the set?

4 Make up a set of data that has:

- five pieces of data
- a range of 16.

5 Parcels of these weights in kg were sent by a company in one day.

      6.8, 12.45, 8.6, 5.25, 4.08, 2.72, 4.5, 6.4, 7.25, 8.6,
      0.75, 0.65, 1.3

a What was the weight of the heaviest parcel?
b Find the weight of the lightest parcel.
c What is the range for this data?

6 *Supertram* sells Adult tickets, Child tickets and Saver tickets. This table gives the data for the type of tickets sold over a weekend.

	Adult	Child	Saver
Friday	35	6	35
Saturday	68	39	43
Sunday	76	72	57

a Find the range for the adult ticket data.
b Find the range for the child ticket data.
c Find the total number of saver tickets sold.
d Find the mean for the saver ticket data.

9.5 Comparing data

You can compare two sets of data using the average and the range.

Example 1

This data gives the number of chips in a serving given by two dinner ladies.

Jenny: 17, 14, 21, 14, 16, 22, 10, 14, 14, 16, 20, 12, 18
Rita: 17, 14, 17, 15, 18, 15, 16, 12, 16, 19, 17

Which of the two would you choose to be served by?
Give reasons for your answer.

Find the mean number of chips per serving for each server.

Jenny: total number of chips 208,   number of servings 13
           mean number of chips per serving $208 \div 13 = 16$

Rita: total number of chips 176,   number of servings 11
           mean number of chips per serving $176 \div 11 = 16$

So for Jenny and Rita the mean number of chips per serving is the same.

Look at the range for the two data sets.

Jenny: Range = greatest value – smallest value
                 $= 22 - 10$
                 $= 12$

Rita: Range = greatest value – smallest value
                 $= 19 - 12$
                 $= 7$

So the data for Rita has a smaller range than the data for Jenny.

Which server to choose?

The mean number of chips they serve is the same but the range for Rita is smaller so these servings are more consistent. So, it is probably best to choose Rita to serve your chips!

Example 2

This data gives the wages paid to the workers in a small firm for one week.

Wages: £175, £206, £92, £108, £86, £475, £51, £48, £55

The firm says the average wage is about £145.
Do you think the workers are happy with this claim?
Explain your answer.

The mean for the data is given by:

    Total of the values ÷ number of values

    Mean = £1296 ÷ 9

         = £144

But the range for the data is large:

    Range = £475 − £48

         = £427

So the mean is being increased by the one large value in the data set.

The median for the data set is given by:

The data in order is:

    £48, £51, £55, £86, £92, £108, £175, £206, £475
      4 values   ↑   4 values
         The median value £92.

The median value is £92.

So it is better to say the average wage is £92.

Exercise 9.5A

1 In a fitness final two teams had to do step-ups for one minute. This is the data for the teams.

Team A	1	2	3	4	5	6	7	8	9	10
Step-ups	44	51	63	48	52	62	53	48	50	59

Team B	1	2	3	4	5	6	7	8
Step-ups	48	53	53	57	54	52	45	54

  a Calculate the mean for each data set.
  b Find the range for each data set.
  c Which team do you think is the fitter? Give your reasons.

2 This data gives the amount spent by a group of customers in a store:

Amount spent:

  £44.70, £58.62, £75.39, £166.44, £84.60, £16.28, £23.67

a Find the range.

b Find the mean.

c Find the median.

The store claims that:

  These customers spent an average of about £67.

d Which average do you think the store used?
Explain your answer.

e Do you think this is a fair claim? Explain your answer.

Exercise 9.5B _____

1 You are one player short in your basketball team.
You must choose either Al or Joel.
This data shows their recent point scores:

  Al: 22, 6, 18, 16, 20, 12, 18, 12, 14, 24, 4, 8, 4, 14, 8, 8
  Joel: 12, 14, 13, 16, 12, 14, 22, 18, 14

a Find the mean for each player.

b Find the range and median for each player.

c Who would you choose for your team?
Give reasons for your answer.

2 A solar-powered car was tested on five days.
The distance travelled in three hours was recorded for each day.

Day	1	2	3	4	5
Distance travelled (km)	263	238	24	193	202

A headline in a paper said: 'Solar car does an average of 184 km in 3 hours'. Do you think this headline is fair?
Give reasons for your answer.

Revision Exercise 9   *Review*

1 This data shows the number of people visiting a cash machine.

Day	Frequency of use
Monday	28
Tuesday	32
Wednesday	44
Thursday	20
Friday	24
Saturday	52
Sunday	16

a Show this data on a bar chart.

b Draw a pictogram for the data.   *Unit 9.1*

2 This bar chart shows the number of students late for school in one week.

a How many students were late on Thursday?

b On which days were fewer than 10 students late?

c How many lates were recorded in total for the week?

d Show the data with a pictogram.

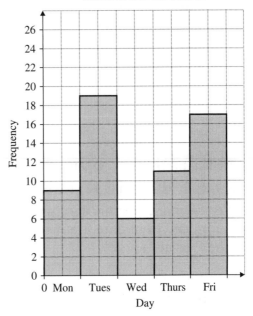

Graph to show the number of students late for school

Unit 9.1

3 This pictogram shows the number of cars using a ferry each day for a week. Show this data on a bar chart.

Monday	🚗 🚗 🚗 🚗
Tuesday	🚗 🚗 🚗 🚗
Wednesday	🚗 🚗 🚗 🚗 🚗 🚗 🚗
Thursday	🚗 🚗 🚗
Friday	🚗 🚗 🚗 🚗 🚗 🚗 🚗
Saturday	🚗 🚗 🚗
Sunday	🚗

🚗 stands for 8 cars

Unit 9.1

4 This data gives the height of water above low
water mark as the tide rises.

Review

Time	Height (cm)
15.00	0
15.30	22
16.00	34
16.30	39
17.00	46
17.30	53

Draw a bar line graph to show the data.

Unit 9.2

5 This pie chart shows the number of visits
made to a bowling alley in a year by a
group of 60 people.
Estimate:

a how many people made 4 visits

b how many people made 1 visit

c the number of people making more
than 3 visits.

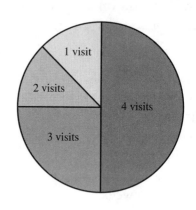

Unit 9.3

6 These are the marks for a group in a test.
Mark:　4, 6, 7, 10, 14, 11, 12, 15, 6

a What is the mode for this data set?

b How many pieces of data are there?

c Find the median mark.

Unit 9.4

7 Find the mode and median for this data set.
12, 23, 19, 21, 18, 15, 12, 14, 17, 23, 25, 11, 10, 12

Unit 9.4

8 What is the range for this data set?
15, 23, 21, 19, 24, 11, 17, 22, 19, 29, 16, 17, 17, 22

Unit 9.4

9 A data set has a lowest value of 43.
The range for the data set is 65.
What is the largest value in the data set?

Unit 9.4

10 This data gives the number of items in baskets   ***Review***
at a supermarket checkout.

7, 11, 23, 16, 3, 21, 19, 4

a Calculate the range for the data.
b Calculate the mean for the data set.   *Unit 9.4*

11 A cyclist spent three days touring the Cotswolds.
The mean distance travelled each day was 84 km.
On day 1 a total of 92 km was cycled.
On day 3 a total of 54 km was cycled.

How far was cycled on day 2?   *Unit 9.4*

12 You are one player short in your basketball team.
You must choose Chester or Larkin.
This data shows their recent point scores.

Chester   16, 22, 4, 8, 9, 14, 17
Larkin   12, 15, 14, 11, 8

a Find the mean and median for each player.
b Find the range for each player.
c Which player would you choose for your team?
Explain why.   *Unit 9.5*

Investigation

Headlines

This headline was found in a local paper.

Survey shows girls look after their teeth better than boys

Carry out your own survey to check out the claim made by the paper. You will need to
think about:

- how you will collect your data
- how you will present your data in a report
- how you will explain what your data shows.

10 PROBABILITY

10.1 The 0 to 1 probability scale

▶ Probability is a measure of how likely something is to happen.
You can use it to predict the chances of an event happening in
the future.

▶ Any probability can be shown on a scale from 0 to 1:

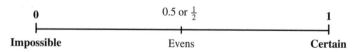

▶ An event with an **evens** chance of happening is just as likely to happen as not
happen.
There is an evens chance that when a normal coin is spun it lands heads up.

Exercise 10.1A

1 Say if you think each of these events is either:

impossible, very unlikely, unlikely,
evens, likely, very likely, certain.

a There will not be a cloud in the sky tomorrow.
b The next person you meet in the corridor will be female.
c The next person you phone will be out.
d The next person you meet in school will be younger
than 20.
e You will go to Mars on holiday this year.
f When you drop a slice of bread it lands butter side down.
g Your heart will beat more than 10 times in the next hour.

2 Give an example of an event with less than an 0.5 chance
of it happening.

3 Give an example of an event with a probability of 0.

4 Tony says the probability of a car having three doors is
0.9. Does this seem about right to you? Explain.

5 a Put these in order of probability. Start with the least likely.

- The next person you meet will be left-handed.
- A man over 60 will be balding.
- A computer will crash when you use it.
- A letter will be sent by First Class mail.
- Tomorrow you will clean your teeth.
- A school text book will be less than 1 cm thick.

b Which of the events is closest to evens?

Exercise 10.1B

1 Sasha says that the probability of him being ill this winter is 0 as he is never ill.
Why is this not true?

2 Give an example of an event which is certain.

3 The arrow shows a probability scale with the probability that a person will have a telephone.

Sketch probability scales with arrows to show what the approximate probabilities for each of these will be:

a A person picked at random will cycle to school.
b A ship will hit an iceberg on its maiden voyage.
c A pupil will eat chips at school today.
d A football player in the premiership will be male.
e A vegetarian will eat beef today.
f A cat will be sleeping when you next see it.

4 It is very difficult to give an event with a probability of exactly 1 or 0. Give reasons why these events might not have probabilities of exactly 0 or 1.

a You will climb Mount Everest in your lifetime.
b You will meet a green man with two heads.
c A piece of paper will catch fire if you put a lighted match to it.
d A car will run well if it is in good condition.

5 Give an event with a probability that is exactly:

a 1   **b** 0   **c** $\frac{1}{2}$

10.2 Events and outcomes

An event can have different outcomes.
For example:
These are six possible outcomes from the roll of a dice.

    1, 2, 3, 4, 5 or 6.

> Rolling the dice is an **event**. The number on the dice is an **outcome**.

▶ Some outcomes can be **equally likely**.
For example, getting a 6 is as equally likely as getting a 4 or a 3.

▶ Other outcomes are **not equally likely**.
For example, getting an even number has 3 chances (2, 4 or 6) but getting a number less than 3 has only 2 chances (or 2).
So these two outcomes are not equally likely.

Exercise 10.2A

1 a List the possible outcomes when you spin a coin.
  b Are these outcomes equally likely? Explain why.

2 a List the outcomes when you roll a 0 to 9 dice.
  b Are these outcomes equally likely?

3 You go to a supermarket. Is it equally likely that you will go to Asda, to Tesco or to Sainsbury's? Give reasons for your answer.

4 Alison throws a dart at a dartboard.
Some of the outcomes are that she scores 20, 4, 50 or 60.
Are these outcomes equally likely? Explain your answer.

5 Three runners, Chris, Dave and Afzal run a 200 metre race.
Why are the outcomes: Chris wins, Dave wins, Afzal wins, not equally likely?

Exercise 10.2B

1 a Give two outcomes when you turn the ignition key in a car.
  b Are these outcomes are equally likely? Explain.

2 Rachael has 2 red jumpers, 1 blue jumper and 3 yellow jumpers in a drawer. She pulls one out the drawer without looking at it.

   a What different outcomes could she get?

   b Are these outcomes equally likely? Give your reasons.

3 A 1 to 10 dice is spun. Are these outcomes equally likely:

   a a 6 or a 9

   b a prime number or an odd number

   c a square number or a multiple of 3?

> For information on primes, squares and multiples see pages 21 to 25.

10.3 At random

▶ Taking something from a box **at random** means picking so that every item has an equal chance of being picked. If each item feels the same and you keep your eyes shut then you will pick at random.

▶ A number that you get with a fair dice is a random number because each side has an equal chance of being on top.

Exercise 10.3A

1 Which of these is picking at random? If you think it is not explain why not.

   a Spinning a coin to decide who goes first in a game.

   b Picking who washes up from the colour of people's shoes.

   c You need a painter. You use a pin in the painter's section of Yellow Pages.

   d You need to pick a letter of the alphabet at random. You open a book and stick a pin in the page. You choose the letter it lands on.

2 Is picking straws a fair way to decide who goes first? Explain your answer.

Exercise 10.3B

1 Five people go on a camping holiday for three days.
One of them wants to use these spinners to decide who
empties the toilet each day.

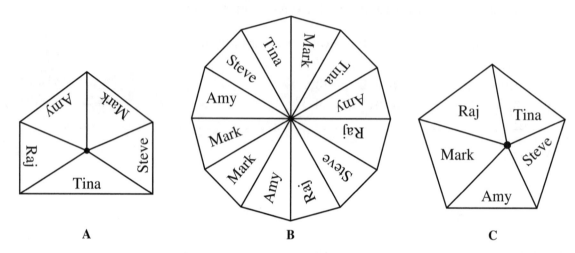

A   B   C

  a For each spinner explain why it does not give a random
      choice.
  b Which person do you think made the spinners?
      Explain why.

10.4 Calculating probabilities

▶ When outcomes are equally likely you can calculate
probabilities.

Example

This five-sided spinner has sides of equal length.
Calculate the probability that it will land on a cross.
There are 5 sides and each side is equally likely.
(They are all of equal lengths).

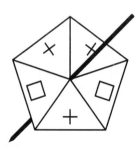

The probability of the spinner landing on any one side
is '1 out of 5' or $\frac{1}{5}$.
But there are 3 crosses.
So the probability of the spinner landing on a cross is $\frac{3}{5}$.

Exercise 10.4A

1 Give the probability that the spinner on p. 214 lands on a square?

2 This eight-sided spinner is spun.
Calculate the probability that:

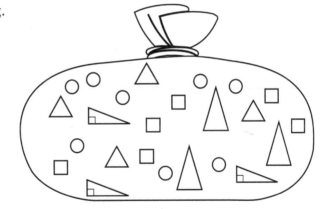

   a it lands on a five-pointed star
   b it lands on a star
   c it lands on a circle with a dot in it
   d it lands on a circle
   e it lands on no side
   f it lands on a side that is not a star
   g it lands on a side that is not a six-pointed star

3 A box has six blocks in it, all the same.
Three blocks are red, two are green and one is yellow.
A block is picked out at random.
Find the probability, that it is:

   a red   **b** yellow   **c** green
   d blue   **e** not red   **f** a colour

4 This shows the shapes in a bag.
A shape is picked at random.
Give the probability that it is:

   a a square   **b** a circle
   c a triangle   **d** not a square
   e an equilateral triangle
   f a right-angled triangle

Exercise 10.4B

1 This diagram shows the socks in a drawer.

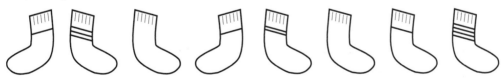

A sock is pulled out at random.
What is the probability that it has:

   a one stripe   **b** two stripes   **c** no stripes
   d some stripes   **e** a sock shape   **f** one like it still in the drawer?

2 There are six cars for sale: 1 red, 3 blue and 2 white.
Sally likes red so she buys the red car.
Why is the probability that Sally buys a red car not $\frac{1}{6}$?

3 This 1 to 6 dice is rolled.
What is the probability of getting:

a a six   **b** an even number
c an eight   **d** a number less than 5
e an odd number   **f** a multiple of 2
g a number greater than 4   **h** a number that is not greater than 4?

4 A 20-sided dice is numbered 1 to 20.
Each score is equally likely.
What is the probability that with one roll of this dice
your score will be a prime number?

10.5 Probability experiments

▶ The **theoretical probability** that you get a head when you spin a fair coin is $\frac{1}{2}$ or 0.5.
If a coin is fair, in 20 spins you should get ten heads.

> A fair coin is one that is not biased by weights or has two heads.

$$20 \times \tfrac{1}{2} = 10$$

When you do an experiment to test this it may not work out to be the same.

Exercise 10.5A

1 a Spin a coin 20 times and record your results in a table like this.

	Tally	Frequency
Number of Heads		
Number of Tails		

b Is the result what you expected?
Will spinning the coin more times help?
Explain your answer.
c Spin your coin an extra 80 times and record the results.
How did this change your results? Explain.

2 If a fair dice is rolled six times it will come up with a different number each time.

   a Do you agree? Explain your answer.

   b Do an experiment by rolling a dice 100 times.
Is the dice a fair dice? Explain your answer.

Exercise 10.5B

1 You spin a fair coin 1000 times.

   a Do you expect to get 500 heads? Explain your answer.

   b If you get 1000 heads what might you say about the coin?

2 **a** When you roll a dice what is the theoretical probability that you will score either a 5 or a 6?

   b In 30 rolls of the dice how many times would you expect to score either a 5 or a 6?

   c Test this with an experiment and make a frequency table that records the two options:
(5 or 6) and (not 5 or 6).

   d Were the results as you expected?

   e How could you improve the accuracy of your experiment?

Revision Exercise 10 *Review*

1 Say if you think each event is:

impossible, very unlikely, unlikely,
evens, likely, very likely, or certain.

   a The bell will ring at the end of the school day.

   b You will be late for school tomorrow.

   c You will eat chips today.

   d The next person you meet will be wearing a tie.

   e You will travel to school tomorrow by bike.

   f The next person you meet will be from the planet Zog.   *Unit 10.1*

2 Give an example of an event with a probability of 1.   *Unit 10.1*

3 Give an example of an event with a probability of 0.5.   *Unit 10.1*

4 a List all the outcomes when you roll a 1 to 6 dice.
  b Are the outcomes equally likely? Explain why.

Review
Unit 10.2

5 A spinner has the numbers 0 to 9 around the edge.
Are these outcomes equally likely:

  a a 5 or a 6
  b a multiple of 2 or a multiple of 3
  c an odd number or a prime number?

Unit 10.2

6 Give an example of picking at random.

Unit 10.3

7 A box has ten beads inside, all are the same size.
3 beads are blue, 2 are red, 1 is yellow and 4 are green.
A bead is picked from the box at random.

Give the probability that it is:

  a red
  b yellow
  c green
  d blue
  e not red
  f not green
  g blue or yellow
  h red or yellow
  i black
  j not yellow.

Unit 10.4

SATS Paper 1 – Non Calculator – Time 1 hour

1

| 6 | 1.0 | 0.5 | $\frac{1}{4}$ | 0.4 | $\frac{1}{2}$ | 0.3 | 0.5 |

Using only numbers from these cards copy and complete each of these.

a ☐ is equal to ☐

b ☐ is half of ☐

c ☐ – ☐ = 0.2

d ☐ + ☐ = 1.4

e ☐ × ☐ = 6.0

f 5 ÷ ☐ = 10

(6 marks)

2 For a garden fence, rods are made into triangles.
These are then fixed with bolts.

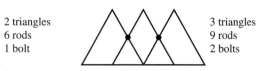

1 triangle
3 rods
0 bolts

2 triangles
6 rods
1 bolt

3 triangles
9 rods
2 bolts

a A fence has 5 triangles. How many rods are used? (1 mark)

b A different fence uses 24 rods. How many triangles are made? (1 mark)

c When 10 bolts are used how many triangles are made? (1 mark)

d A fence has 5 bolts. How many rods are used? (2 marks)

e If b = number of bolts, r = number of rods and t = number of triangles, which two of these are true?

A $t = 3r$ B $b = t - 1$ C $t = b - 1$

D $r = 3t$ E $r = t + b$ F $b = 3r - 1$ (2 marks)

3 Here are three rectangles:

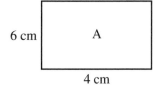

6 cm   A   4 cm

w B   7 cm

3 cm   C l

a Calculate the area of rectangle A. (1 mark)

b Calculate the perimeter of rectangle A. (1 mark)

c Rectangle B has an area of 35 cm². What is its width w? (1 mark)

d Rectangle C has a perimeter of 28 cm. What is its length l? (2 marks)

4 A single pen costs £1.45.

£1.45

a How much will 5 single pens cost?   (1 mark)
b How many single pens could you buy with £20?   (1 mark)
c In packs of 2, pens cost £2.78.
   How much does each pen cost?   (1 mark)
d Calculate the cheapest cost of buying 9 pens.   (2 marks)

5 There are 3 red sweets, 4 blue sweets and 5 green sweets in a
bag. A sweet is picked at random.

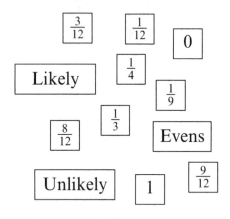

Choose one of the labels above for the probability that:
a the sweet is yellow.   (1 mark)
b the sweet was bought at a shop.   (1 mark)
c the sweet is one most people don't like.   (1 mark)
d the sweet is red.   (1 mark)
e the sweet is not blue.   (1 mark)

6 This table gives the amount per hour earned by six people.

Alison	Barry	Clare	Dave	Ellen	Fred
£6.25	£5.50	£12	£7	£4.50	£8

a How much does Barry earn for working 6 hours?   (1 mark)
b How much in total do they all earn per hour?   (1 mark)
c Clare and Fred both work for 8 hours each day.
   How much more does Clare earn per day?   (1 mark)
d Barry pays 10% of his wage to his mum.
   How much does his mum get for every hour Barry works?   (2 marks)
e $\frac{1}{5}$ of Alison's wage is taken for tax.
   How much does she keep for each hour she works?   (2 marks)

7 This graph shows sales of three types of bread over a week.

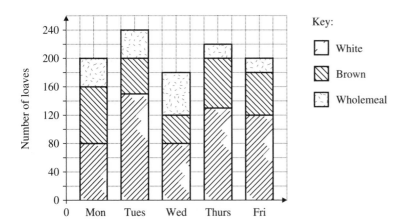

Key:

☐ White

▨ Brown

▨ Wholemeal

   a How many loaves of each type were sold on Wednesday?   (1 mark)

   b How many more white loaves were sold on Thursday then Wednesday?   (1 mark)

   c What fraction of the loaves sold on Friday were brown bread?   (1 mark)

   d What percentage of the loaves sold on Monday were wholemeal?   (1 mark)

8 Lisa puts the number 142 in her calculator. She multiplies the number by 100.

   a Copy the display and show the missing digits.

                                             (1 mark)

   b Now she clears the display and enters the number

     She divides this number by 10.
     Show how the display looks now.   (1 mark)

   c Lisa can use the digits 4, 7, 2, 5, 3 in any order.
     Copy this display to show the largest number she could make.

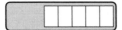

                                             (1 mark)

   d Now copy the display and show the smallest number she can make.   (1 mark)

9 Look at these eight cards.

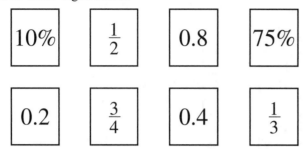

   a Which card shows the largest amount? (1 mark)
   b Which two cards show the same amount? (1 mark)
   c Which is larger: $\frac{1}{2}$ or $\frac{1}{3}$? (1 mark)
   d List the cards in order starting from the smallest amount. (2 marks)

10 Machine A multiplies an input by 6.

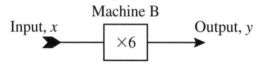

   a Give the output when the input is 5. (1 mark)
   b Give the input when the output is 24. (1 mark)

Machine B does two things.

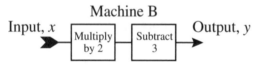

   c Give the output when the input is 7. (2 marks)
   d Copy and complete this formula for machine B:
   $y = \boxed{}\, x \, \boxed{}\, 3$ (1 mark)

11 Toni has found a quick way to work out this problem in her head.
   72×20
She uses the sum $72 \times \blacksquare \times \blacktriangle$ where $\blacksquare$ and $\blacktriangle$ are numbers

   a What sum does she use? (1 mark)
   b Calculate the answer using Toni's method. (1 mark)

Mark uses a different quick method.
He uses $72 \times 100 \div \blacktriangledown$ where $\blacktriangledown$ is a different number
   c What number is Mark using for $\blacktriangledown$? (2 marks)
   d Write down a simple sum you could use to work out
      14×300 in your head. (1 mark)

12 This graph shows a line where the x coordinate is always
1 smaller than the y coordinate.
For example, at the point (2, 3) x is 2 and y is 3.

  a Give the coordinates of the other dots on the line.   (1 mark)
  b Another point on the line has the coordinates (67, ☐).

    What is the value of ☐ ?   (1 mark)

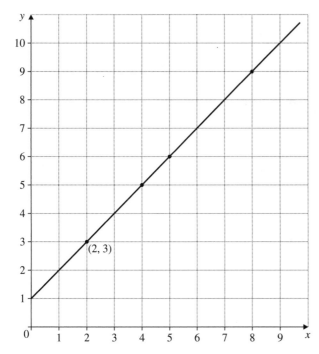

  c Copy the graph and mark 3 points where the x coordinate is
2 more than the y coordinate.   (2 marks)
  d Draw a line through your points.
    Would this line go through the point (17, 19)? Explain your answer.   (1 mark)

13 Copy each shape and draw in **all** its lines of symmetry.

  a 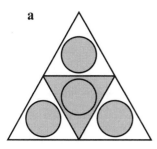   **b** 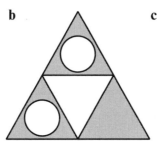   **c**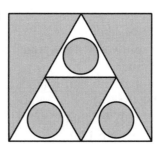

                                                   (3 marks)

                                          Total 66 marks

SATS Paper 2 – Calculator allowed – Time 1 hour

1 The words in LOGO for drawing this
pentagon from point C anticlockwise are:

**FD 40, LT 90, FD 38, LT 45, FD 28,
LT 90, FD 28, LT 45, FD 3.8, LT 90**

where **FD** means Forward and **LT** means Left.

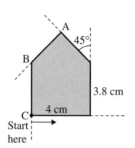

  a Explain what FD 40 means.   (1 mark)
  b How long in centimetres is the side AB?   (1 mark)
  c Martin gives the words to draw a rectangle
     5 cm long by 4 cm wide.
     He starts with FD 50, RT 90, …
     Give the words to draw all the rectangle.   (2 marks)
  d Give the LOGO words to draw a square of side 3 cm.   (2 marks)
  e These words draw a shape:
     FD 10, RT 90, FD 10, LT 90, FD 10,
     RT 90, FD 20, RT 90, FD 20
     Use square paper to draw the shape.   (2 marks)

2 Look at this spinner with 5 sides.
  a Which numbers on the spinner are even numbers?   (1 mark)

Clare spins the spinner.
  b Give the probability that the spinner will land
     on an even number.   (1 mark)
  c What is the probability that it lands on a
     number greater than 6?   (1 mark)
  d What is the probability that it will land on
     a number greater than 12?   (1 mark)
  e Give the probability that it does **not** land on 9 or 7.   (1 mark)
  f What is the probability that it lands on a number?   (1 mark)

3 Wayne used these questions in a survey on pets.

Q1 'What pets do you have?'
Q2 'Do you have a lot of pets?'
Q3 'Do you take good care of your pets?'

a Say what is wrong with each question.   (3 marks)
b Write each question so it would provide better data for Wayne.   (3 marks)

4 On each side of a square, the number in the middle is the sum
of the numbers one each end of it.

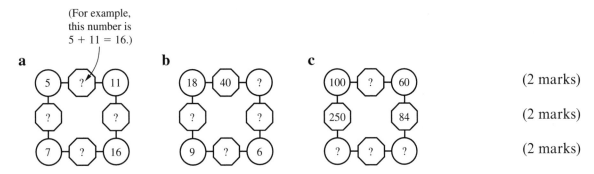

(For example,
this number is
5 + 11 = 16.)

a   **b**   **c**   (2 marks)

(2 marks)

(2 marks)

Copy each square and fill in the missing numbers.

5 This is a sequence of patterns with white and black dots.

Pattern 1   Pattern 2   Pattern 3

a Draw pattern 4.   (1 mark)
b How many white dots will be in pattern 12?   (1 mark)
c How many black dots will be in pattern 12?   (1 mark)
d What is the total number of dots in Pattern 10?   (2 marks)

Sarah uses these number machines to find the total number of
dots in a pattern.

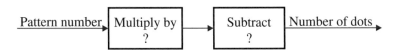

Pattern number → | Multiply by ? | → | Subtract ? | Number of dots →

e Copy and complete the machines.   (1 mark)

6 Ali listed the birds she saw in one day.

Bird	Frequency
Wren	8
Sparrow	
Starling	44
Blackbird	12
TOTAL	80

a How many sparrows did she see? (1 mark)

b In its simplest form, what fraction of the birds seen were wrens? (1 mark)

Ali made a pictogram for the birds she saw. She has completed it for Sparrows and Starlings.

c What does a 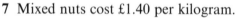 stand for? (1 mark)

d Copy and complete the pictogram. (2 marks)

7 Mixed nuts cost £1.40 per kilogram.

a How much does this bag of mixed nuts cost? (1 mark)

b A sack of mixed nuts costs £21.
How many kilograms are in the sack? (1 mark)

This scale shows the weight of nuts in a box:

5 kg   6 kg

c What weight of nuts is in the box? (1 mark)

d How much would this weight of mixed nuts cost? (1 mark)

The diagram shows a bag of cob nuts.

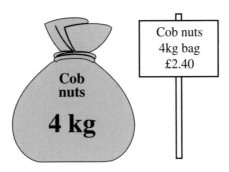

e How much would a 5 kg bag cost? (2 marks)

8 Find the value of each missing number.

a $743 - \boxed{} = 379$ (1 mark)

b $42 \times \boxed{} = 714$ (1 mark)

c $326 + 493 + \boxed{} = 1200$ (1 mark)

d $\boxed{} \div 33 = 11$ (1 mark)

e $\dfrac{\boxed{}}{\boxed{}}$ of $759 = 253$ (1 mark)

f $\frac{3}{4}$ of $\boxed{} = 120$ (2 marks)

9

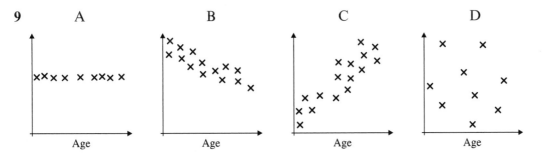

These scatter graphs show how things change with the age of a car.
Which graph could show:
a The cars' value against its age? (1 mark)
b The number of breakdowns against its age? (1 mark)
c The road tax paid over a car's age? (1 mark)
d The diameter of the steering wheel against its age? (1 mark)
e Sketch a scatter graph that might show the total distance
travelled for 12 cars of different ages. (2 marks)

10 The perimeter of this shape is $4a + 2b$.

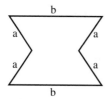

Write expressions for the perimeter of these shapes.

a
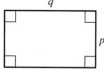

b
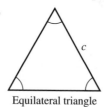

Equilateral triangle

c
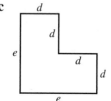

d
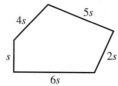

(4 marks)

e This shape has a perimeter of 29 cm.
What is the value of f?

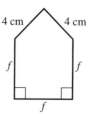

(2 marks)

Index